IVAN MOSCOVICH

BrainMatics

MORE

LOGIC
PUZZLES

h.f.ullmann

PUZZLE NUMBERS

The puzzles in this book are accompanied by two numbers in a small box: a white box which indicates the puzzle number and a red box which indicates the puzzles difficulty. If you are searching for the solution of a special puzzle in the solutions part, you can easily identify the solution by the number in the white box.

All puzzles in this book have been designed and carefully checked by the author.

© 2009 Tandem Verlag GmbH
h.f.ullmann is an imprint of Tandem Verlag GmbH

Idea & Concept: Ivan Moscovich
Text: Ivan Moscovich
Project Coordination: Daniel Fischer
Layout: scripta, Cologne
Cover Design: Jeff Beebe

Printed in China

ISBN 978-3-8331-5374-7

10 9 8 7 6 5 4 3 2 1

www.ullmann-publishing.com

"Imagination is more important than knowledge. Knowledge is limited."
Albert Einstein

EINSTEIN ON MATH

"Never before in my life have I troubled myself over anything so much. I have gained enormous respect for mathematics, whose more subtle parts I considered until now, in my ignorance, as pure luxury!"

Einstein, in a letter to a friend, 1916

"Our experience hitherto justifies us in believing that nature is the realization of the simplest conceivable mathematical ideas. I am convinced that we can discover by means of purely mathematical constructions the concepts and the laws connecting them with each other."

(Einstein in the Herbert Spencer lecture at Oxford, 1933)

Necessity, it has been said, is the mother of invention. But does this apply to creativity too? A pragmatist might say it does because, after all, there's no difference between invention and creativity, so that's the end of the matter.

But somehow this simple answer doesn't seem to be enough, at least where mathematics is concerned. While there is no question that invention involves creativity, is it really true that NECESSITY is always the underlying cause?

One cannot disagree that necessity may be part of the story, at least sometimes, but experience suggests there is a lot more going on as well. And nowhere is this more obvious than in the creativity that lies at the heart of mathematics.

BrainMatics

Archimedes may have cried "Eureka!" when he found the answer he needed to the challenge of working out the volume of an irregular object, specifically the volume of the crown of the king of Syracuse, as the story tells us. But in this book we can also see that as well as many other mathematical inventions he also created an extraordinary geometrical board game, which appears here with the name Stomachion. Where was the strict necessity for that?

The missing ingredient, I suggest, is curiosity. The stimulus, one may guess, began with a simple question, "what if?"… the question which all curiosity begins.

It's probable that some kind of interactivity is another factor, because we all know that new ideas flow more freely when they are shared and "brain-stormed" with others. However, there are also many instances where extraordinary creativity just happens alone, when thoughts circle round and suddenly a new idea pops up. Even if the creative mind is working away furiously in the background, as far as perceptible cause is concerned, the creation seems to come out of the blue. So interactivity may, or may not, be a requirement. But curiosity is something creativity cannot manage without. Curiosity, furthermore, is a powerful human force – possibly even one of the most important things that make us who we are.

It seems to me that curiosity is what drives the mathematical mind more than anything else. The unceasing, wrangling urge to look at something differently, to test a formula to destruction if that's possible, and to seek endlessly for a more efficient, more elegant, more beautiful solution than has ever existed before.

This book has many marvellous qualities, among them its ability to explain and inspire love for a science that is all too often made obscure. But, even more, I am convinced that its ability – its inevitability – to stimulate curiosity in "the beautiful science" will prove to be its most valuable quality of all.

BRAINMATICS

CONTENTS

The numbers following the puzzles' titles indicate the puzzles and their rankings. The puzzles' numbers are set bold, the ranking is set in italics. The numbers are corresponding to the red and white boxes on the puzzle pages.

"Beauty is the first test: there is no permanent place in the world for ugly mathematics."
G.H. Hardy (1877–1947)

"Mathematics is more than a tool and a language for science. It is also an end in itself, and as such, it has, over the centuries affected our worldview in its own right."
Stephen Hawking

"I do not feel I have wisdom enough yet to love what is ugly."
Stendhal (1783–1842)

"I want you to fall in love with mathematical ideas, to begin to feel seduced by them, to see how easy it is to be entranced and to want to spend years in their company, years working on mathematical projects."
Gregory Chaitin in Metamaths

"HARMONOGRAMS OF MOSCOVICH"

Created in collaboration with a MACHINE – an analog computer, the famous Art-Drawing Machine, a world-patented invention, which got its first wide exposure at the **Cybernetic Serendipity** exhibition in London, 1969, a milestone event in modern art history – and the **HUMAN ARTIST**.

THE HARMONOGRAPH OF MOSCOVICH
US Patent 3,473,229

The Harmonograph, invented in 1955 using an analog computer, is a unique mechanical instrument that draws high-quality paintings of great beauty and artistic value. Each Harmonogram, as the machine's paintings are called, is a unique original, even today unsurpassed by any other techniques including use of the modern electronic computer.

In the 1970s and 1980s the Harmonogram paintings were exhibited and acclaimed at major art exhibitions and one-man-machine shows all over the world:

Cybernetic Serendipity, ICA in London

International Design Centre, Berlin

Museum of Modern Art, Mexico City

Didacta Exhibition, Hanover, Germany

Israel Museum, Jerusalem

Technorama, the Swiss Science Center in Winterthur, has built Moscovich's Harmonograph as one of its key permanent interactive exhibits (shown right).

In the 2000s the Harmonograms of Hila Moscovich, art creations made by the daughter of the inventor using an improved design of the original patented Harmonogaph of Moscovich, created a renewed interest in harmonograms.

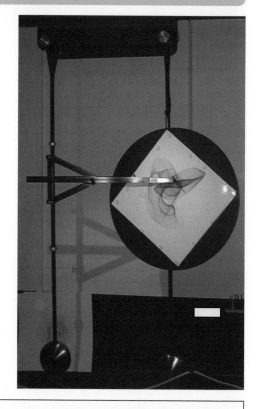

"For the idea of this drawing machine (US Patent No 3,473,229) we must thank Ivan Moscovich, the former director of the Museum of Science and Technology, Tel Aviv. He first presented it in 1968 in a brilliant exhibition of art and computer technology, Cybernetic Serendipity, where Jean Tinguely also exhibited."

Acknowledgement at Technorama

MAGIC SQUARES

LO-SHU – The oldest and unique magic square

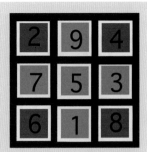

Arrangements consisting of numbers in square pattern so that the sum of the numbers in each row, column, and sometimes diagonals are called magic squares.

The oldest magic square is the Chinese **"Lo Shu"** dated c. 2000 BC. It is a magic square of order-3 and its pattern is unique.

Chinese literature dating from as early as 2200 BC tells the legend of Lo Shu or "scroll of the river Lo". In ancient China, there was a huge flood. The people tried to offer some sacrifice to the river god of one of the flooding rivers, the Lo river, to calm his anger. Then, there emerged from the water a turtle with a curious figure/pattern on its shell; there were circular dots of numbers that were arranged in a three by three nine-grid pattern such that the sum of the numbers in each row, column and diagonal was the same: 15.

The sum of 9 digits in Lo-Shu adds up to 45, which divided by 3 gives you the **"magic constant"** of 15.

In general, this constant for any order n magic square can easily be found using the formula:

$$M = \frac{n(n^2+1)}{2}$$

There are 8 possible triads of digits that add up to 15:

9+5+1   9+4+2   8+6+1   8+5+2   8+4+3   7+6+2   7+5+3   6+5+4

The center digit belongs to four lines. Five is the only digit to appear in four triads and therefore it must be the center digit.

Digit 9 is in only two triads. Therefore it must go in a middle side cell which gives us the complete middle column: 9+5+1.

3 and 7 are also in only two triads. The remaining four numbers can fit in only one way - proving elegantly the uniqueness not counting rotations and reflections of the Lo-Shu solution.

DÜRER'S DIABOLIC MAGIC SQUARE

An order-4 magic square

The most famous magic square is Dürer's Diabolic Magic Square. Albrecht Dürer included his magic square in his engraving *Melancholia* (1514). It is called diabolic because it is much, much more "magic" than the definition of a magic square requires it to be.

How many different geometrical patterns of four numbers can you find totaling the magic constant of 34?

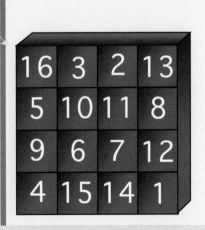

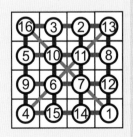

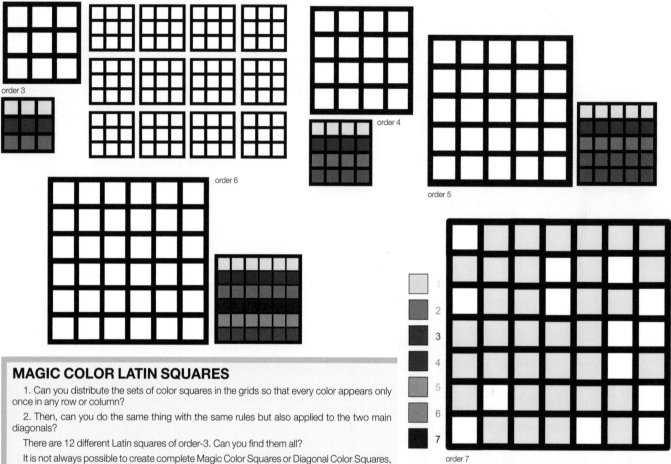

order 3

order 4

order 5

order 6

order 7

MAGIC COLOR LATIN SQUARES

1. Can you distribute the sets of color squares in the grids so that every color appears only once in any row or column?

2. Then, can you do the same thing with the same rules but also applied to the two main diagonals?

There are 12 different Latin squares of order-3. Can you find them all?

It is not always possible to create complete Magic Color Squares or Diagonal Color Squares, in which case the object is to find the best solution (i.e., the largest possible number of colors which can be fitted in the particular square.

LATIN AND GRECO-LATIN MAGIC SQUARES

Leonhard Euler (1707-1783), one of the most famous mathematicians of all time, near the end of his life invented two new variations of magic squares, Latin and Greco-Latin magic squares. Latin magic squares are square matrices on "n" rows and columns in which different symbols, numbers, colors or anything else are so arranged that no symbol occurs more than once in any row or column, and sometimes also in the two main diagonals. A Greco-Latin magic square is a magic square of two superimposed Latin magic squares arranged according to two conditions:

1. Every row and every column contains exactly one symbol of the combined squares;

2. No two cells contain the same ordered pair of symbols.

In 1782 Euler constructed Greco-Latin magic squares of order-n, where n is odd or multiple of 4. He also tried to create a Greco-Latin square of order-6 but did not succeed. He came to the conclusion with a conjecture that no Greco-Latin squares of order-6 and higher can exist.

His conjecture was first tested in 1959 when a computer was programmed to search for order-10 Greco-Latin magic squares. It searched for 100 hours and found none, which was not a surprise because it is estimated that a complete search would have taken more than 100 years. However, the next year, in 1960, E.T. Parker, R.C. Bose, and S.S. Shrikhande invented a new computer approach which, surprisingly, produced a wealth of Greco-Latin magic squares of orders higher than 6, among them squares of order-10. This was one of the proud moments of mathematical discovery, and it was also an achievement In terms of the beautiful artistic pattern of the outcome.

COVER-UP

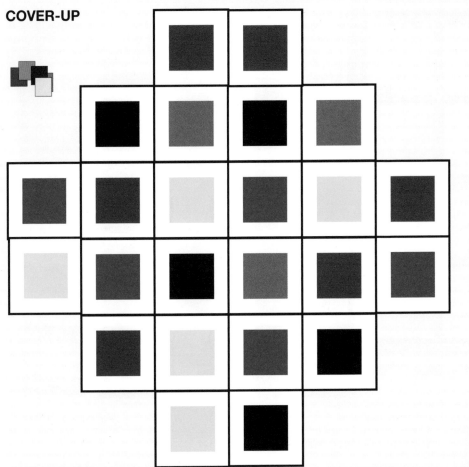

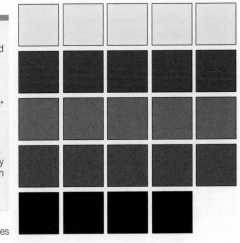

COVER-UP

Cover-Up is a puzzle game of my own invention for up to four players. It was manufactured as a boxed game under the name *Spectrix* in the 1970s and 1980s and is soon to be relaunched, again as *Spectrix*.

The object is to place all 24 colored tiles in the game board.

The rules are as follows:

(1) You cannot place a tile on a square of the same color or next to a square of the same color. ("Next to" includes the four neighboring squares that are adjacent orthogonally – that is, at right angles.)

(2) After each move, a square on the board assumes the color of the tile that covers it.

(3) You cannot place a tile on top of another tile.

One or more players can play. If you are playing with two players, you are the winner if you are still in play when your opponent is unable to place a tile. When playing alone, the object is to place all square tiles in the gameboard under the above conditions.

Patents, Copyrights by Ivan Moscovich

The 24 playing pieces

11

MAGIC COLOR SHAPES

Can you arrange the 16 color shapes provided in the four-by-four square gameboard so that they form four-color/four-shape configurations as illustrated in the six patterns shown and listed below:

(1) 4 vertical columns;

(2) 4 horizontal rows;

(3) 2 main diagonals;

(4) 4 corner squares;

(5) 4 center squares;

(6) 4 quarter squares.

MAGIC COLOR SHAPES

The 16 playing pieces comprise four different shapes – square, hexagon, octagon, and star – with each set in the four colors yellow, red, green, and blue.

004 8

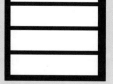

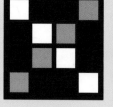

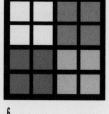

1   2   3   4   5   6

THE SPIDER OF JEREMIAH FARRELL
Magic Hexagons

Puzzle 1 Place consecutive numbers from 1 to 18 on the circuits of the web so that on the three hexagons and on each diagonal the numbers add up to 57.

Puzzle 2 Place the six letters of the word SPIDER on the circuits of the three hexagons and the three diagonals.

©2000 by Jeremiah Farrell, dedicated to Martin Gardner at Gathering for Gardner 6, Atlanta, USA.

MAGIC DICE CUBE OF JEREMIAH FARRELL

A very special kind of magic cube was invented by Jeremiah Farrell. Twenty-seven standard dice are arranged to form a 3-by-3-by-3 cube so that its faces have magic relationships.

The unfolded net of the magic dice cube is shown, revealing all of its faces. It is magic on every face with respect to the rows and columns, as in typical flat magic squares. But it is much more magical in the third dimension. In addition, when the magic dice cube is placed on the table with one of its sides facing up, as in our presentation, it is magic also around its four sides, in a special way.

Choose one of the diagonals, rows, or columns on one side. Then add the four corresponding diagonals, rows, or columns around the four faces. The total will always be 42.

For example, you might choose the second row of a side (top) with 4+1+3 = **8**, plus 2+4+5 = **11**, plus 3+6+4 = **13**, plus 5+3+2 = **10**. **The total is 42**.

It is up to you to check whether these magical properties will work no matter how the magic dice cube is placed on the table.

It will be a rewarding project to get 27 standard dice and glue them together into the magic dice cube.

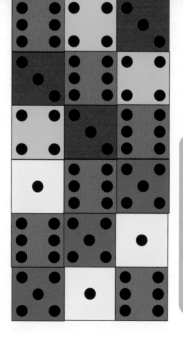

Jeremiah Farrell is Emeritus Professor of Mathematics at Butler University of Indianapolis and still teaches classes on special topics such as combinatorial games, etc. He is a well-known inventor of ingenious puzzles and games. He is also an organizing member of "Martin's People's", meetings at the biannual "Gatherings for Gardner" conferences in Atlanta.

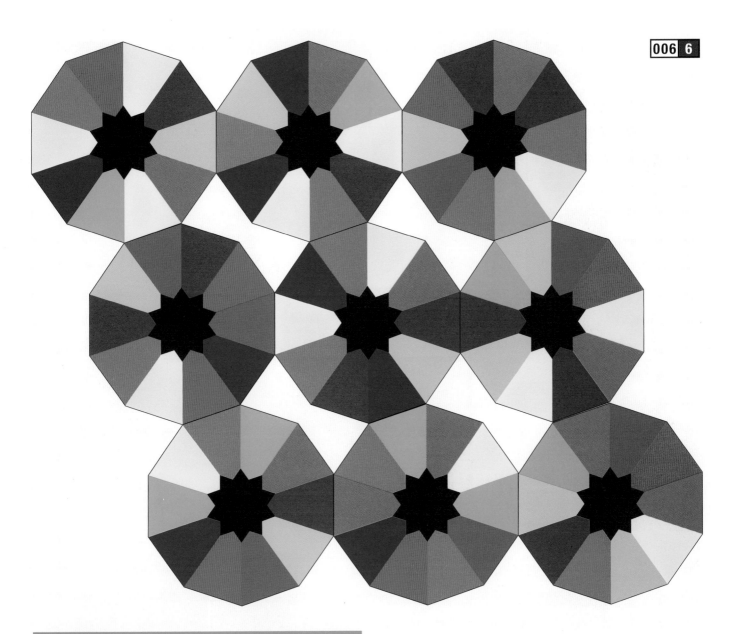

DECAPUZ

Can you copy and cut out the nine decagons and rearrange them into the same configuration, so that all the colors are matching along the touching sides? The shapes should stay where they are – they only need to be rotated.

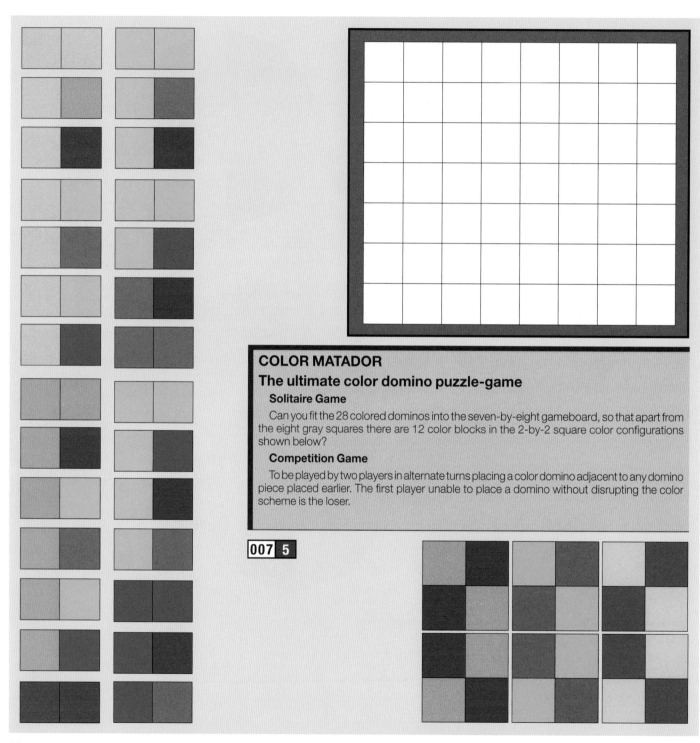

COLOR MATADOR

The ultimate color domino puzzle-game

Solitaire Game

Can you fit the 28 colored dominos into the seven-by-eight gameboard, so that apart from the eight gray squares there are 12 color blocks in the 2-by-2 square color configurations shown below?

Competition Game

To be played by two players in alternate turns placing a color domino adjacent to any domino piece placed earlier. The first player unable to place a domino without disrupting the color scheme is the loser.

007 5

16

GEOMETRIC DISSECTIONS AND TRANSFORMATIONS

What is a geometric dissection? It is when a geometric figure is cut into pieces that can be rearranged to form another, new figure. To cut up a geometric figure and then make a different one with the same area by reassembling the pieces in a different way has interested mathematicians for many centuries. The German mathematician David Hilbert proved that it is always possible if you make enough cuts. The goal of the great puzzle inventors Sam Loyd and Henry Dudeney was to minimize the number of pieces from which such transformations can be obtained. Their goal of minimizing the number of pieces created a competitive craze for finding newer and better solutions, resulting in many exciting puzzles and design approaches.

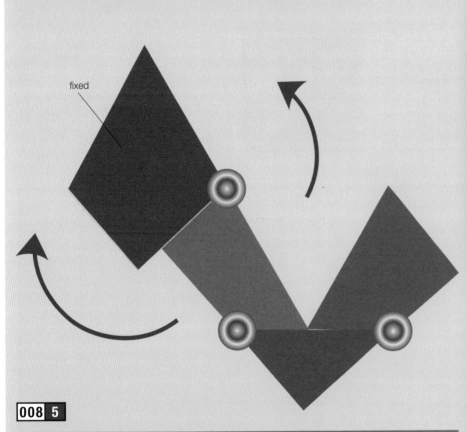

fixed

008 5

HINGED POLYGONS – DUDENEY'S TRANSFORMATION

Four oddly shaped polygons are hinged together, forming the configuration shown. Just by looking, can you tell what the outcome will be when the polygons are rotated about the hinges and closed clockwise and counterclockwise? Will the outcome be the same in both cases?

HENRY ERNEST DUDENEY
(1857–1930)

Author, mathematician, and one of England's greatest inventors and creators of puzzles, Henry Dudeney was Sam Loyd's British counterpart, with whom he exchanged countless ideas and collaborated on many puzzles and articles. Dudeney believed that puzzle-solving is a creative activity of the highest importance for improving thinking and logical decision-making. His finest mathematical achievement was the discovery of a dissection puzzle called "The Haberdasher's Puzzle," which is the puzzle shown here.

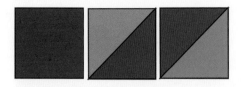

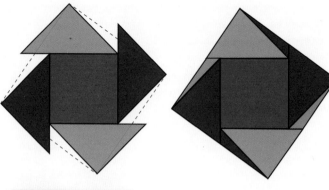

THREE SQUARES INTO ONE

Wefa's ingenious and elegant dissection from the 9th century – a nine-piece dissection.

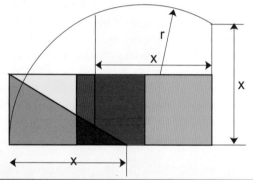

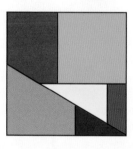

THREE SQUARES INTO ONE

Dudeney's dissection, improving Wefa's dissection, using only six pieces to achieve the solution.

THREE SQUARES DISSECTING POLYGONS

Thinkers must have considered ways of dissecting geometrical shapes thousands of years ago, but the first systematic treatise on the subject seems to be a book by 10th-century Persian astronomer Abul Wefa (940-998CE). Only fragments of his book survive, but they include beautiful dissection problems such as, "Can you dissect three identical squares so that they can be reassembled to make one single big square?"

Wefa's puzzle was the forerunner of one of the most interesting types of geometrical dissections, the problem of dissecting a geometrical figure into another specified figure in the minimal (fewest possible) number of pieces. English mathematician Henry Ernest Dudeney (1857-1930) was the pioneer of this type of puzzle. He solved Wefa's problem using only six pieces. Ever since Dudeney, dissection records have been constantly improving.

There are many ways to divide an area into parts. Some of the ways of making these divisions are particularly interesting.

Putting small shapes together to make larger shapes is also fun – like making a pattern of tiles on a floor. In mathematics, the combination of small shapes to make larger ones is called "tessellation," and it has interesting rules of its own, as we shall see later.

The relationships between the sizes of different shapes that fit together also form rules, which are useful for making calculations, and predicting other relationships. The Pythagorean theorem is based on an observation of this kind.

If two shapes with straight-line edges (polygons, regular or irregular) can be assembled from the same set of pieces by fitting them together in different ways, then it is clear that the areas of the two figures are the same. Conversely, it can also be shown that any two polygons of equal area may be dissected into a finite number of pieces that can then be reassembled to form either of the two original polygons.

The main interest of dissections as recreational math problems is to find how to dissect one figure into another in the minimal number of pieces. Only lately have mathematicians begun to take problems of dissections seriously. The branch of mathematics called dissection theory provides valuable insights into the solutions of many practical problems in plane and solid geometry.

In dissection problems, the pieces may already be given; the object then is to create as many interesting patterns as possible with them. The ancient recreation of tangrams is a good example.

On the other hand, two undissected polygons may be given; then the problem is to find ways to dissect them to transform one into the other. Usually the object is to use as few pieces as possible.

A third and apparently paradoxical variant is to dissect a shape into pieces, remove one piece, and reassemble the remaining pieces to form the original shape. Although this is impossible, many puzzles appear to achieve it.

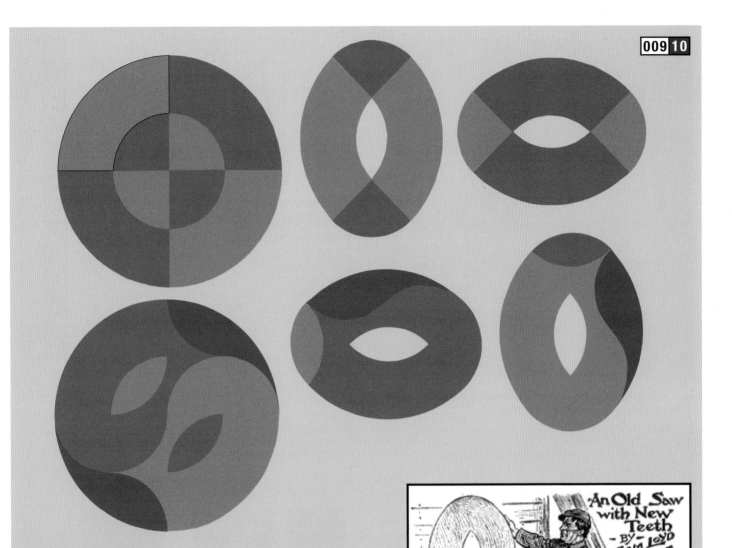

OVAL TABLES

In 1821, in his book *Rational Amusement for Winter Evenings*, John Jackson posed the classic puzzle of how to cut and transform a circular table into two identical oval tables, each with an elongated hole in the middle. His solution is shown at the top, with the table dissected into eight pieces. Sam Loyd in his *Cyclopedia of 5000 Puzzles, Tricks & Conundrums*, solved the puzzle using only six pieces as shown. But he continued to search for a solution that involved a smaller number and soon found an astonishingly elegant four-piece solution. Can you find it?

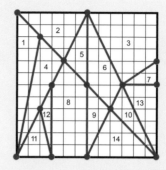

1	
2	
3	
4	
5	
6	
7	
8	
9	
10	
11	
12	
13	
14	

ARCHIMEDES' STOMACHION

This beautiful dissection puzzle, attributed to the ancient Greek philosopher Archimedes (287–212BCE), is called the stomachion, "Archimedes Box," or the "Loculus of Archimedes." It is one of the world's oldest puzzles. According to a tenth-century Greek manuscript, Archimedes wrote a book about the puzzle. The book was lost for more than 2,000 years, but parts have recently been re-discovered, and have aroused great interest.

The puzzle consists of 14 pieces that form a square. As in the ancient Chinese puzzle of tangrams, the object of the game is to rearrange the pieces to form abstract and figurative shapes or patterns. In the Greek manuscript mentioned above, the areas of the stomachion pieces were defined.

The stomachion was originally a geometric dissection problem. The challenge was to divide a square into 14 pieces, so that each piece has an area in a rational proportion to the area of the square. Can you work out the areas of the 14 pieces of the stomachion?

You can copy and cut out the 14 colored pieces of the stomachion (above) to make figures. At top right is the structure of the puzzle with its lattice points on a 12-by-12 square grid. We don't know whether in Archimedes' version of the puzzle a player was permitted to turn the pieces over.

DOUBLING THE AREA OF A SQUARE

Tangram and stomachion

A mathematical theorem reputedly taught by ancient Greek philosopher Socrates (469–399BCE) may have inspired Archimedes to create the stomachion. Plato (428–348BCE) described in his dialog *Meno* how Socrates taught a pupil that to double the area of a square you do not need to double the length of a side of the square. In its simplest form, this mathematical theorem can be demonstrated by the four isosceles right triangles shown below.

There is also an interesting interrelationship between these four isosceles right triangles, the stomachion and the much later tangram puzzle developed by the ancient Chinese. By adding four lines to divide the four triangles, we get the classical seven-piece tangram puzzle shown below, while by adding eight lines, we arrive at the 14-piece stomachion puzzle of Archimedes.

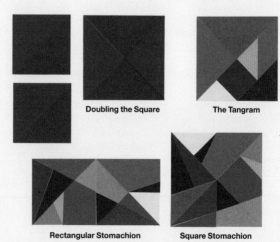

Doubling the Square

The Tangram

Rectangular Stomachion

Square Stomachion

PYTHAGOREAN THEOREM

After Thales, the next major figure in Greek mathematics was Pythagoras (c.572 B.C.- 475 B), who is credited with the proof of the beautiful and important Pythagorean theorem.

However, it's interesting to know that there is proof that Babylonian mathematicians understood the Pythagoran theorem and its relationship to right-angled triangles. The proof comes from a Babylonian clay tablet, known as "Plimpton 322", dated between 1900-1600 B.C., more than a thousand years before Pythagoras was born.

Another crucial contribution of Pythagoras and his followers was the discovery of irrational numbers.

The Pythagorean theorem is considered to be the oldest geometrical theorem of mankind. Its representations are probably the earliest abstract symbols visualizing the transition from the *IDEA* to the *SOLUTION* (and not the other way around), and this symbolizes the beginnings of *real* science of mathematics, based on abstract mathematical thinking. This abstract approach resulted from ancient Babylonian and Egyptian observations that there is a beautiful geometrical relationship and pattern exhibited by all right-angled triangles, and then their ability to both generalize and prove this fact.

The geometric theorem attributed to Pythagoras is one of the select few theorems that almost everybody has at least a nodding acquaintence with. It deals with the relationships between the two shorter sides of a right-angled triangle and the longer side (hypotenuse).

Because the Pythagorean theorem is so famous and important in mathematics, several hundreds of different ways to prove it have been created and published over the centuries. Leonardo da Vinci created an original proof and many other mathematicians are creating them still.

The theorem is stated as: "The square on the hypotenuse is the sum of the squares on the other two sides."

In symbols this can be represented as:

$$a^2 + b^2 = c^2.,$$

where **a** and **b** are the lengths of the two shorter sides, and **c** is the length of the hypotenuse.

A *right-angled* triangle obeys the **Law of Pythagoras**

But what does this actually mean?

In numerical terms, it means that we may construct right-angled triangles by using any three lengths a, b, c that satisfy the Pythagorean condition:

$$a^2 + b^2 = c^2.$$

For example:

$$3^2 + 4^2 = 9 + 16 = 25 = 5^2$$

Therefore, a triangle with sides 3, 4, and 5 is necessarily a right-angled triangle. There are many such whole-number Pythagorean triplets. Geometrically, the Pythagorean theorem also asserts an equality of areas. The square whose side is the hypotenuse c has exactly the same area as the sum of two squares along the other two sides combined.

PYTHAGORAS (569 B.C. - 475 B.C.)

Pythagoras was born on the island of Samos in Greece. Credited by many to be the first pure mathematician, he founded a group or cult known as "the Brotherhood of Pythagoreans". They were fanatically devoted to the study of mathematics. Their motto was "Numbers Rule the Universe". Nothing remains of Pythagoras's written works and details of his life are known only through other writers, some of whom used original sources.

The beliefs held by Pythagoras and his followers were that:
1. at its deepest level, reality is mathematical in nature;
2. philosophy can be used for spiritual purification;
3. the soul can rise to union with the divine;
4. certain symbols have a mystical significance;
5. all brothers of the order should observe strict loyalty and secrecy.

While little is known about Pythagoras himself, it is certain that his school made extremely important contributions to mathematics. In particular, they advanced the general principles of mathematics, the concept of number, the concept of geometrical figures and the abstract idea of mathematical proofs.

BABYLONIAN TABLET (THE YALE TABLET)

Dated from approximately 1800-1600 BC, this tablet proves that the Babylonians knew how to compute the square root of a number (e.g. $\sqrt{2}$) with remarkable accuracy. Even more remarkable, this implies a simple way to calculate the diagonal of a square, by multiplying the side of the square by the square root of 2 ($\sqrt{2}$).

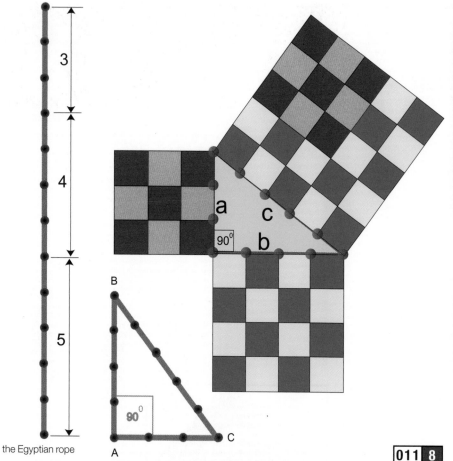

3

4

5

the Egyptian rope

B

A   90°   C

a   c

90°   b

EGYPTIAN TRIANGLE

Using a rope divided with knots into 12 equal parts, the surveyors of ancient Egypt reputedly constructed near-perfect right angles. The triangle they formed with the rope has sides in the ratio 3:4:5. This triangle is often called the "Egyptian triangle," and is used by mathematicians to demonstrate the Pythagorean theorem – "The square on the hypotenuse (the triangle's longest side) is the sum of the squares on the other two sides." A visual proof of the Pythagorean theorem for the Egyptian triangle is shown to the left.

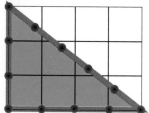

the Egyptian rope stretched into the Egyptian triangle of 6 units area

011 8

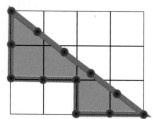

the Egyptian rope stretched into a polygon of 4 units area

EGYPTIAN TRIANGLE AND ROPE PUZZLES

By 2000BCE the ancient Egyptians had a primitive numeral system and some geometric ideas about triangles, pyramids, and so on.

There are unverified historical records of the ingenious ancient Egyptian method of creating right angles. Egyptian surveyors used a loop of rope of 12 units in length, divided into 12 equal parts by knots, to create a right-angled triangle with an area of 6 units: they fixed the rope along a line between A and B and pulled the remaining loop taut at point C. The result was a right angle.

You can use a similar rope to create other shapes.

(1) Can you use the rope to form a straight-sided polygon with an area of four units? One solution is shown; can you find others?

(2) What is the largest area that can be encompassed by the Egyptian rope held straight between points?

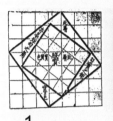

1

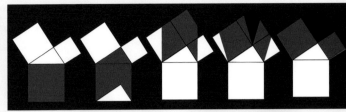

3

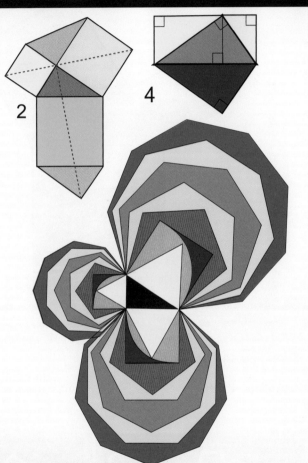

2

4

PYTHAGOREAN THEOREM
The Most Beautiful Proofs

Eli Maor's *Pythagorean Theorem: A 4,000-year History* is the ultimate book on the Pythagorean theorem. Maor writes:

"What is that gives the Pythagorean theorem its universal appeal? Part of it, no doubt, has to do with the great number of proofs that have been proposed over the centuries. Elisha Scott Loomis (1852–1940), an eccentric mathematics teacher from Ohio, spent a lifetime collecting all known proofs – 371 of them – and writing them up in *The Pythagorean Proposition* (1927). Loomis claimed that in the Middle Ages it was required that a student taking his Master's degree in mathematics offer a new and original proof of the Pythagorean theorem. Some of these proofs are based on the similarity of triangles, others on dissection, still other on algebraic formulas, and a few make use of vectors. There are even "proofs" ("demonstrations" would be a better word) based on physical devices; in a science museum in Tel Aviv, Israel, I saw a demonstration in which colored liquid flowed freely between the squares built on the hypotenuse and on the two sides of a rotating plexiglass-made right triangle, showing that the volume of liquid in the first square equaled the combined volume of the other two. But there is another reason for the universal appeal of the Pythagorean theorem, for it is arguably the most frequently used theorem in all of mathematics."

A selection of celebrated visual proofs of the Pythagorean theorem is reproduced here.

(1) This statement of the theorem was discovered on a Babylonian tablet dated c.1900 BCE, many centuries before the time of Pythagoras (c.572–475BCE). Pythagoras is credited with being the first to provide a proof of the theorem – this was probably a proof by dissection, similar to the beautiful one in the *Chou Pei Suan Ching* ("Arithmetic Classic of the Gnomon and the Circular Paths of Heaven"), an ancient Chinese manuscript dated c.200BCE.

(2) This proof was devised by Italian polymath Leonardo da Vinci (1452–1519).

(3) In 1945 New York mathematician Hermann Baravalle published a five-step dynamic proof.

(4) The simplest proof, this was devised by American physicist Stanley Jashemski, at the age of 19. It was reinvented by Eli Maor as "the folding bag."

Can you understand and explain these proofs?

PYTHAGOREAN THEOREM
Generalized forms

We know that the areas of the two squares on the sides of a right-angled triangle are equal to the area of the square on the hypotenuse. But it is a lesser-known fact that the validity of the Pythagorean relationship holds also for an endless number of other figures (so long as they are geometrically similar). Some of these are shown above.

PYTHAGORAS

PYTHAGORAS
Turn the triangle to show that...
"The square on the hypotenuse is equal to the sum of the squares on the other two sides".

Turn really hard

PYTHAGOREAN THEOREM DEMONSTRATION MODEL SERIES
Classical and generalized forms

The series provides physical three-dimensional demonstrations of the validity of the Pythagorean relationships, using colored liquid flow from one compartment to the other two.

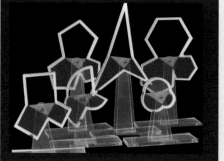

DYNAMIC DEMONSTRATION MODELS
Science can be Art

In the late 1950s I invented and patented a set of demonstration models for the basic physical and mathematical principles of science and, specifically, of fluid mechanics.

Physics demonstrations in classrooms usually require a great deal of work and preparation. They involve bulky equipment and setups and often result in just one single demonstration in one run. The basic concept of my "Dynamic Demonstration Models" was to avoid this and streamline classroom demonstrations. The models were hermetically sealed, thin transparent boxes, filled with liquids and other moving parts, visually demonstrating and proving phenomena. The models could be reused and the demonstrations repeated any number of times.

The Israeli company Orda Industries manufactured the models until the late 1970s. Initially intended as classroom aids, the models soon came to be valued as science toys, puzzles, and even kinetic art objects. Some of the models, specially designed in a bigger size, became highly successful art pieces and aroused great interest at kinetic art exhibitions and science museums worldwide – including Cybernetic Serendipity in London (1968) and Didacta in Basel (1970). Indeed, some of these models – such the Pythagorean theorem demonstration model series and the "HexCell" sculpture that demonstrates phenomena of minimal soap structures – can still be found today at science museums.

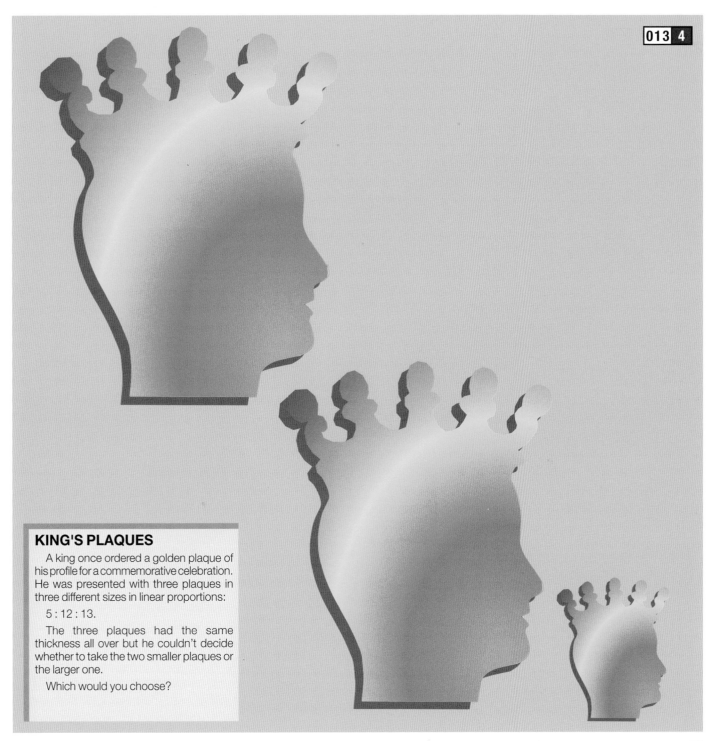

KING'S PLAQUES

A king once ordered a golden plaque of his profile for a commemorative celebration. He was presented with three plaques in three different sizes in linear proportions:

5 : 12 : 13.

The three plaques had the same thickness all over but he couldn't decide whether to take the two smaller plaques or the larger one.

Which would you choose?

THE PYTHAGOREAN CURIOSITY

In his celebrated book *The Pythagorean Proposition* Elisha Loomis included a composition he called "The Pythagorean Curiosity." I have based this design on Loomis' "Curiosity," adding to it an element of infinity.

In addition to the classical Pythagorean theorem, Loomis found in the design several further geometrical relationships of lengths and areas such as:

• the yellow triangles and the Pythagorean triangles are equal in areas;

• the violet trapezoids are equal in areas;

• the two red squares equal five blue squares in area, and so on.

(Loomis traced the curiosity to one John Waterhouse, a New York engineer in the late 19th century).

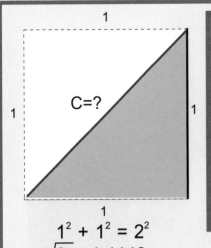

$$1^2 + 1^2 = 2^2$$
$$\sqrt{2} = 1.4142$$

C=?

IRRATIONAL NUMBERS DISCOVERY

Whole numbers and fractions (numbers that can be written as a ratio of two whole numbers) are called "rational numbers." Numbers that cannot be written as fractions are called "irrational numbers."

The Ancient Greeks assumed that any length or area they calculated would be rational – that is, that it could be expressed by a rational number. The Pythagoreans (followers of the 6th-century BCE mathematician Pythagoras) were fascinated by right-angled triangles: they measured the diagonal of a square of unit side and discovered that they could not express this length as a rational number. Ancient Greek mathematician Hippasus of Metapontum (c.500BCE), who was a dedicated Pythagorean, used the Pythagorean theorem to prove that the diagonal of a square with rational sides does not have a rational length. Hippasus is generally credited with the discovery of irrational numbers.

The hypotenuse of a right-angled triangle with sides of one unit is 1.4142… This is an irrational number known as "Pythagoras' Constant." It cannot be written as a fraction and is a recurring decimal number with no pattern of repetition.

Pythagoras' Constant is useful to determine the diagonal of a square of any size. Multiply the length of a square's side by Pythagoras' Constant to calculate the length of the square's diagonal.

NUMBER LINE

NATURAL NUMBERS ⟩ WHOLE NUMBERS   INTEGERS ⟩
ZERO ⟩   positive-negative   RATIONALS ⟩
                                    FRACTIONS ⟩   REAL NUMBERS ⟩
                                              IRRATIONALS ⟩

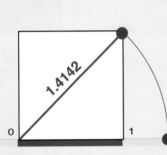

1.4142

-1   0   1   **1.4142**   2   3   4

Can you find an irrational number on the number line, for example the square root of 2?

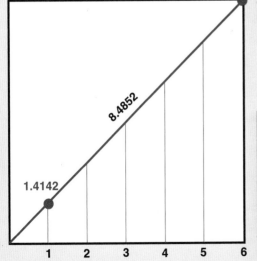

8.4852

1.4142

1 2 3 4 5 6

DIAGONAL OF A SQUARE

Can you determine the length of the diagonal of a square that has sides six units long?

You can do this using the Pythagorean theorem.

$$C^2 = A^2 + B^2 = 6^2 + 6^2 = 72$$

$$C = \sqrt{72} = 8.4852\ldots$$

But could you have come to the same answer in a much easier and quicker way?

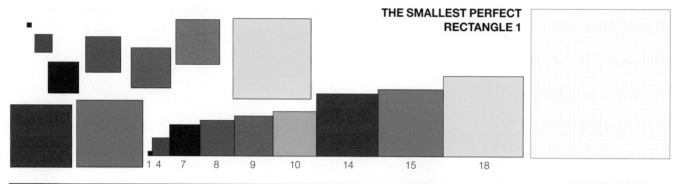

THE SMALLEST PERFECT
RECTANGLE 1

1 4   7   8   9   10   14   15   18

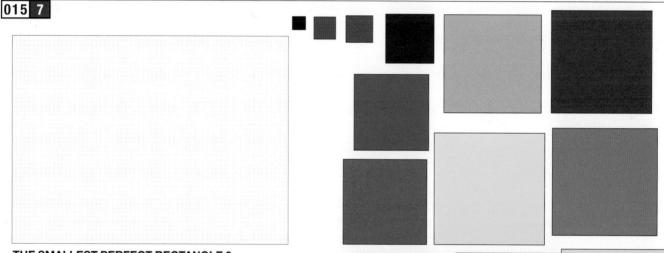

THE SMALLEST PERFECT RECTANGLE 2

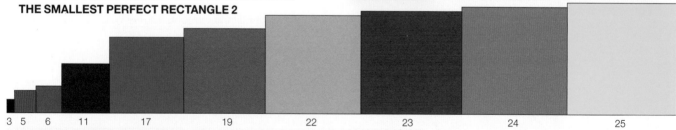

3 5   6   11   17   19   22   23   24   25

PERFECT RECTANGLES

Can a rectangle be subdivided into non-identical smaller squares? In 1903 German mathematician Max Dehn proved the theorem that if a rectangle is dissected into squares, then the sizes of the squares and of the rectangle itself are commensurable – when one is divided by the other, they produce a rational number.

In 1909 Zbigniew Moron discovered a rectangle dissectable into nine different squares and in 1940 Tutte, Brooks, Smith, and Stone proved this be the "smallest," meaning that no smaller rectangle can be divided into nine different squares, and no rectangle at all can be divided into eight or fewer different squares.

The smallest perfect rectangle is composed of squares of sides **1, 4, 7, 8, 9, 10, 14, 15** and **18** units (top). Morón also found the next smallest perfect rectangle, which can be tiled with 10 squares of sides **3, 5, 6, 11, 17, 19, 22, 23, 24** and **25**. (bottom)

The constituent squares for both rectangles are given. Can you put these together to form the two rectangles and so discover their proportions?

28

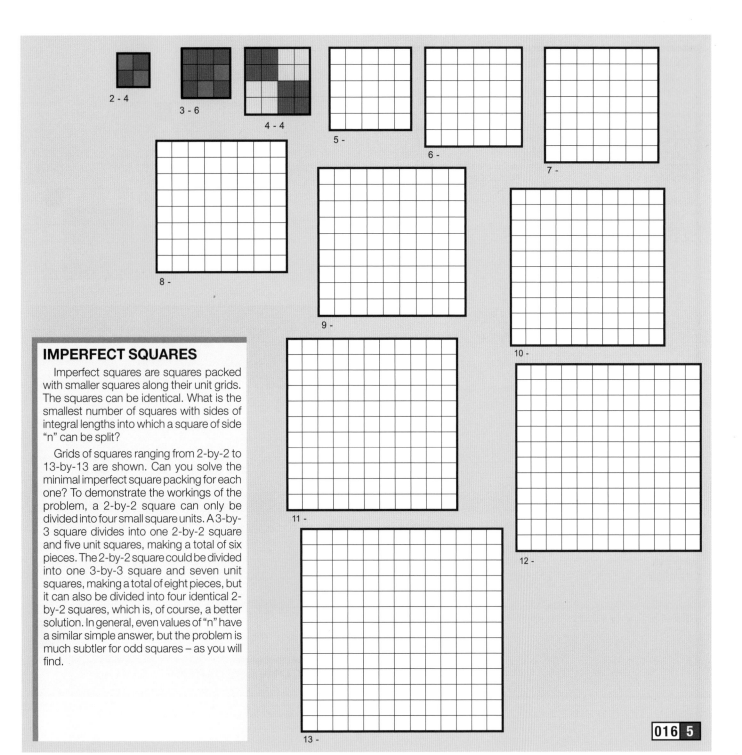

2 - 4

3 - 6

4 - 4

5 -

6 -

7 -

8 -

9 -

10 -

11 -

12 -

13 -

IMPERFECT SQUARES

Imperfect squares are squares packed with smaller squares along their unit grids. The squares can be identical. What is the smallest number of squares with sides of integral lengths into which a square of side "n" can be split?

Grids of squares ranging from 2-by-2 to 13-by-13 are shown. Can you solve the minimal imperfect square packing for each one? To demonstrate the workings of the problem, a 2-by-2 square can only be divided into four small square units. A 3-by-3 square divides into one 2-by-2 square and five unit squares, making a total of six pieces. The 2-by-2 square could be divided into one 3-by-3 square and seven unit squares, making a total of eight pieces, but it can also be divided into four identical 2-by-2 squares, which is, of course, a better solution. In general, even values of "n" have a similar simple answer, but the problem is much subtler for odd squares – as you will find.

016 5

29

CONSECUTIVE SQUARES

We have already dealt with problems involving tessellating a plane with non-identical squares. A very special case and a gem of recreational mathematics is the puzzle involving consecutive integral squares starting from side 1 and up to a set limit.

Can a large square be found that can be completely covered without overlap by such a sequence of smaller squares?

Let's experiment: Squares of sides 1 and 2 cannot form a square: the best we can do is to fit them inside a square of side 3 leaving some empty space. Similarly, squares of sides 1, 2, or 3 cannot fill a square without leaving an empty space; nor can 1, 2, 3, or 4. The first requirement to solve this problem is to add up the areas of the consecutive squares until the result is a square number.

But

$$1^2 + 2^2 = 5;$$
$$1^2 + 2^2 + 3^2 = 14;$$
$$1^2 + 2^2 + 3^2 + 4^2 = 30.$$

None of these is a perfect square.

If we continue the series and go far enough, we find eventually that

$$1^2 + 2^2 + 3^2 + 4^2 + \ldots 24^2 = 4900 = 70^2.$$

In fact, astonishingly, this is not only the first but also the only way to add consecutive squares and obtain a square for the total. (The demonstration is a difficult exercise in number theory, and was itself an unsolved problem for a considerable time.)

The fact that the areas of the first 24 consecutive squares equal the area of a 70-by-70 square, raises the following beautiful geometrical puzzle:

Is it possible to pack 24 consecutive squares starting from a square of unit side into the 70-by-70 square?

Equality of areas is a necessary condition – but might not be sufficient. In fact, a complete packing has not yet been found. Nor has the problem yet been proved to be impossible.

The problem might therefore be rephrased: how many of the first 24 squares is it possible to pack into the 70-by-70 square? The best answer known to date is "all but one," and in every known example it is the 7-by-7 square that is left out, as the example on the following page shows. Can you do better? Twenty-four distinct solutions of this kind exist, but it is still not known if a better way of packing can be found, omitting squares totaling a smaller area than 7x7=49.

To tackle this beautiful problem, cut out a set of 24 consecutive squares from stiff cardboard with sides from 1 to 24 centimeters. Now draw a 70x70 centimeter square and divide it into unit squares. Try to place as many of the cardboard squares as you can, without overlaps.

The 70x70 square is the only square number that ever appears in the sum of consecutive square numbers. You can continue adding more squares but the sum will never become again a square number, a fascinating counterintuitive fact proven in 1918 by English mathematician GN Watson (1886–1965). Therefore, if there is a solution it must be the 70-by-70 square, which so far seems unlikely.

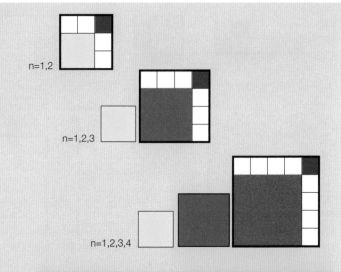

n=1,2

n=1,2,3

n=1,2,3,4

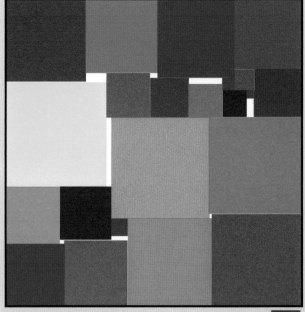

7

CONSECUTIVE SQUARES

The artwork shows the best known solution to the problem: the first 1,2,3, ..., 24, consecutive squares packed in the 70-by-70 gameboard with only the 7-by-7 square left out.

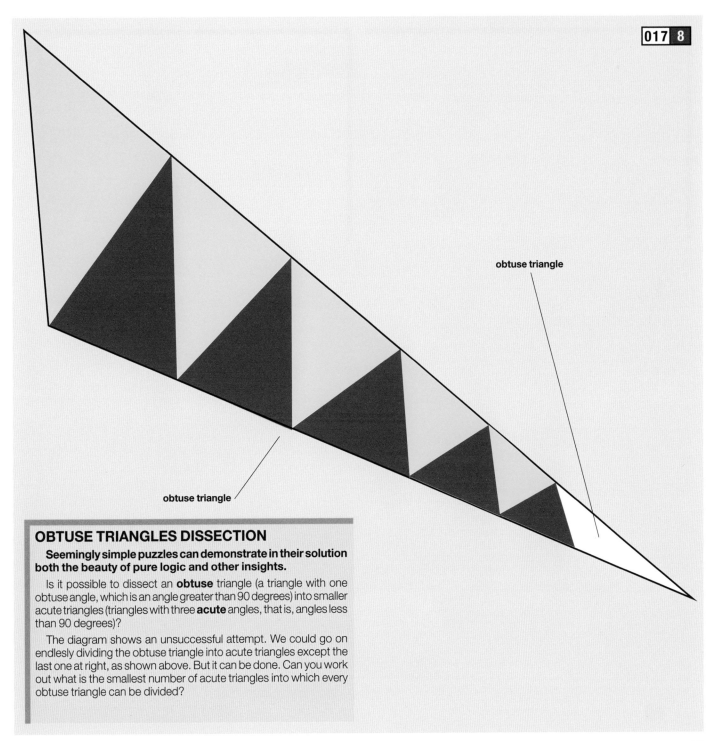

obtuse triangle

obtuse triangle

OBTUSE TRIANGLES DISSECTION

Seemingly simple puzzles can demonstrate in their solution both the beauty of pure logic and other insights.

Is it possible to dissect an **obtuse** triangle (a triangle with one obtuse angle, which is an angle greater than 90 degrees) into smaller acute triangles (triangles with three **acute** angles, that is, angles less than 90 degrees)?

The diagram shows an unsuccessful attempt. We could go on endlesly dividing the obtuse triangle into acute triangles except the last one at right, as shown above. But it can be done. Can you work out what is the smallest number of acute triangles into which every obtuse triangle can be divided?

EQUILATERAL TRIANGLES DISSECTION

Imperfect Triangles

Can you dissect the equilateral triangles along the grid lines into the smallest number of equilateral triangles? None of them will be "perfect," i.e. have all the triangles of a different size.

Perfect Triangles

W.T. Tutte and his colleagues proved that an equilateral triangle cannot be "perfect" and cannot be dissected into equilateral triangles all of different sizes (ignoring orientations). At least two triangles will be of the same size and in the same orientation. However, equilateral triangles can tile in two orientations, in up or down directions. If these are considered as different, since they are not congruent, even if their sizes are identical, then a kind of "perfect" triangle can be found. Tutte found such a "perfect" triangle – the smallest of which is an equilateral with sides of 39 units – all different if orientations of the triangles are considered as different. Its outline grid is shown in the next page.

The Dissection of Rectangles into Squares by R.L. Brooks, C.A.B. Smith, A.H. Stone, and W.T. Tutte in Duke *Mathematical Journal*, vol. 7

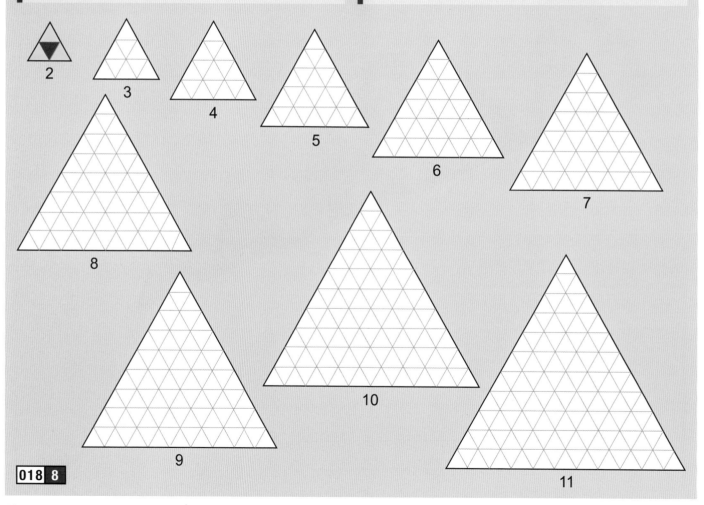

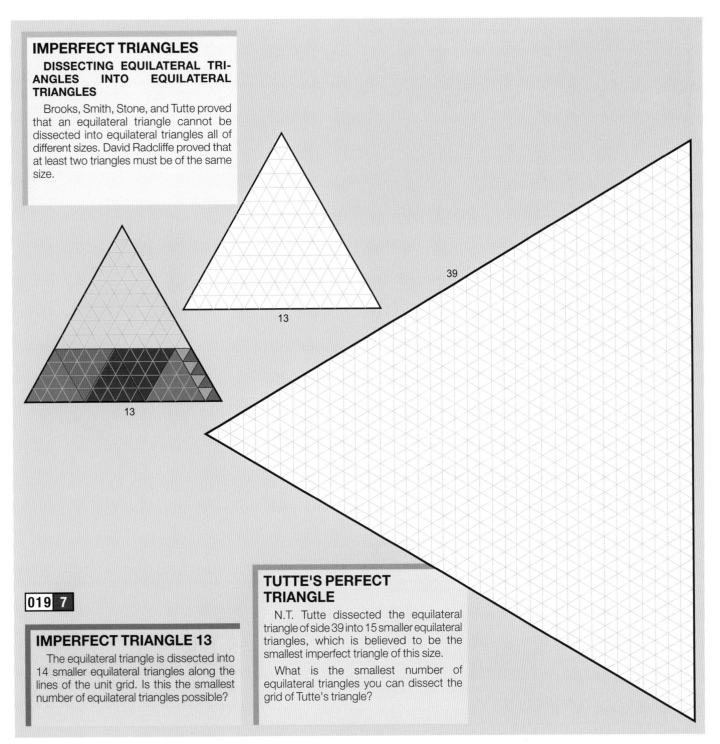

IMPERFECT TRIANGLES

DISSECTING EQUILATERAL TRIANGLES INTO EQUILATERAL TRIANGLES

Brooks, Smith, Stone, and Tutte proved that an equilateral triangle cannot be dissected into equilateral triangles all of different sizes. David Radcliffe proved that at least two triangles must be of the same size.

13

13

39

IMPERFECT TRIANGLE 13

The equilateral triangle is dissected into 14 smaller equilateral triangles along the lines of the unit grid. Is this the smallest number of equilateral triangles possible?

TUTTE'S PERFECT TRIANGLE

N.T. Tutte dissected the equilateral triangle of side 39 into 15 smaller equilateral triangles, which is believed to be the smallest imperfect triangle of this size.

What is the smallest number of equilateral triangles you can dissect the grid of Tutte's triangle?

GEOMETRICAL VANISHES

Many optical tricks and perceptual illusions fail to hold our attention for long because the secret of their trickery is obvious. But the remarkable group of images known as "geometrical vanishes" are so subtle that they continue to intrigue and surprise us even after their workings have been explained.

Sam Loyd (1841–1911), the greatest of American puzzle creators, was the originator of the most famous "vanish" of this kind, the "Get Off the Earth" puzzle. Canadian puzzling genius Mel Stover (and many others) perfected the art, creating subtle variations.

Geometrical paradoxes involve separating and rearranging parts of a total length or area. After rearrangement, a portion of the figure seems to have somehow disappeared. The explanation lies in the "principle of concealed distribution," as Martin Gardner has named it, which depends on the eyes' tolerance for the rearranged version. Often the eyes fail to notice a tiny increase in the gaps between the parts or in the lengths of the reassembled pieces, and so believe that both have the same length or area. Apart from exciting puzzles, the method of concealed distribution was once misused to make 15 $100 bills from only 14, by cutting each into two parts and gluing one part to the next. Please, don't try it!

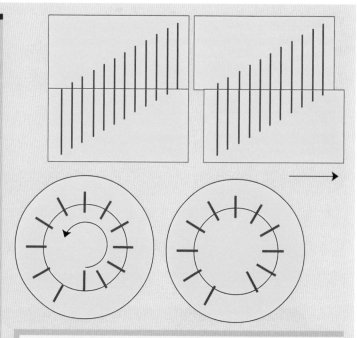

GEOMETRICAL VANISHES

The Secret

Top: 12 vertical lines become 11 when the bottom half is shifted to the right.

Bottom: 12 radial lines become 11 when the inner wheels rotate one notch counterclockwise.

Obviously in both cases nothing has really disappeared. The patterns are only rearranged, and part seems to disappear. The two examples demonstrate the effects of concealed distribution that lie behind many seemingly magical vanishing tricks and paradoxes. They convincingly demonstrate the most elementary principle in geometry: that the whole is equal to the sum of its parts, no matter how the parts are rearranged.

DISAPPEARING FACE MAGIC

Copy the illustration and cut it along the black line. Slide the lower strip one face to the right. All the hats are still there, but one of the faces disappears.

020 2

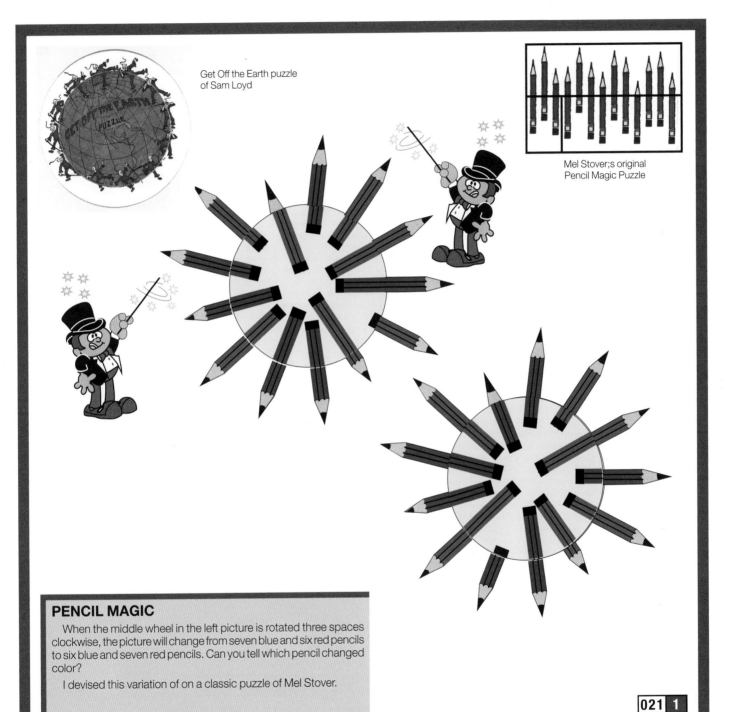

Get Off the Earth puzzle
of Sam Loyd

Mel Stover;s original
Pencil Magic Puzzle

PENCIL MAGIC

When the middle wheel in the left picture is rotated three spaces clockwise, the picture will change from seven blue and six red pencils to six blue and seven red pencils. Can you tell which pencil changed color?

I devised this variation of on a classic puzzle of Mel Stover.

021 1

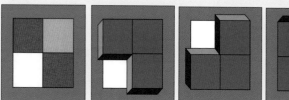

n=1

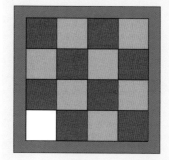 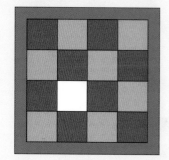 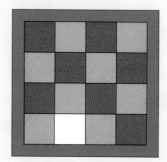 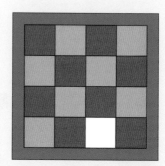

n=2

PACKING TROMINO CHESSBOARDS

The L tromino covers three squares of a chessboard of any size. It is often called the right tromino. We shall be dealing with the problem of packing L trominos into chessboard of dimensions:

$2^n \times 2^n$ for any n>1

Remove a single square from such a chessboard and cover the rest of the board with the appropriate number of L trominos.. Can this be achieved with every chessboard of the above dimensions, no matter which square is removed?

For **n =1**, we have a 2-by-2 chessboard and For **n =2**, we have a 4-by-4 chessboard, as shown above. For **n =3**, a we have a standard 8-by-8 chessboard. Can you cover the chessboard with trominos no matter where the missing square occurs?

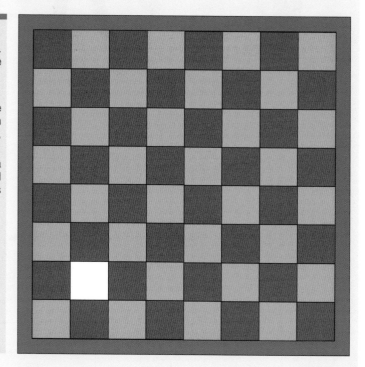

n=3

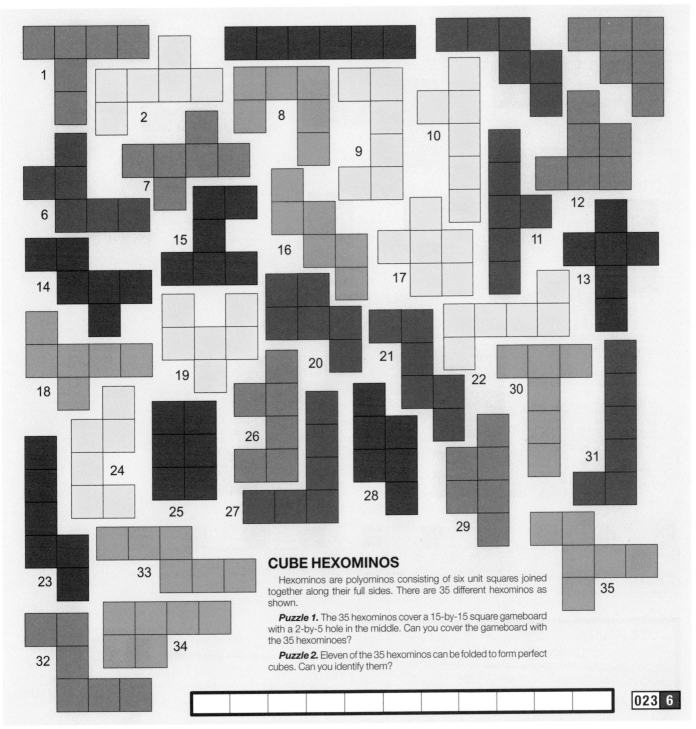

CUBE HEXOMINOS

Hexominos are polyominos consisting of six unit squares joined together along their full sides. There are 35 different hexominos as shown.

Puzzle 1. The 35 hexominos cover a 15-by-15 square gameboard with a 2-by-5 hole in the middle. Can you cover the gameboard with the 35 hexominoes?

Puzzle 2. Eleven of the 35 hexominos can be folded to form perfect cubes. Can you identify them?

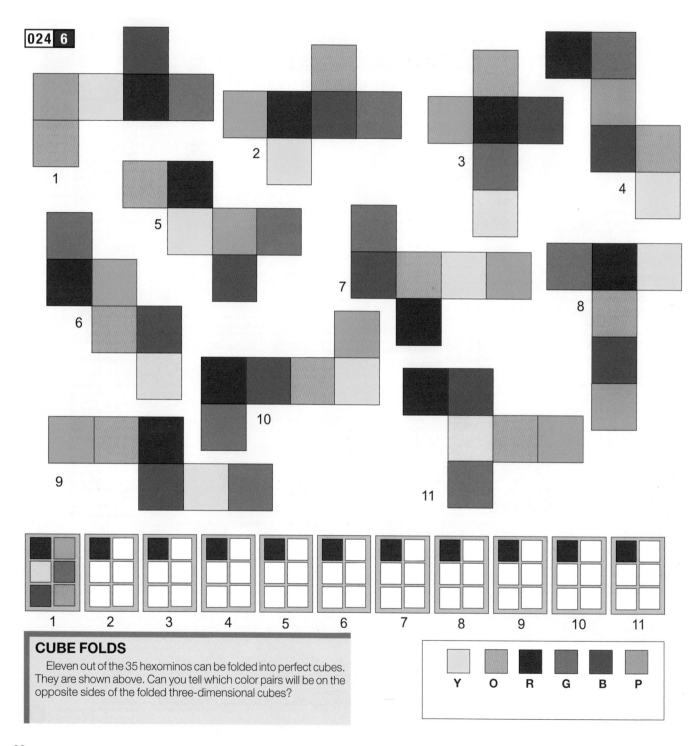

024 6

CUBE FOLDS

Eleven out of the 35 hexominos can be folded into perfect cubes. They are shown above. Can you tell which color pairs will be on the opposite sides of the folded three-dimensional cubes?

Y   O   R   G   B   P

38

STEPPING STONES

The Puzzle

By joining a monomino, a domino, and a straight tromino, how many different configurations can you create? The game provides the following rules and restrictions:

1) The orientation of the pieces must stay vertical.
2) The shorter of the two adjacent pieces may not extend past the edge of the longer piece.
3) Mirror reversals are considered to be different.
4) Pieces must line up along an imaginary grid with squares the size of the monomino.
5) All three pieces must stay connected.

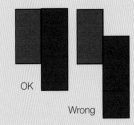

OK

Wrong

STEPPING STONES
The two sets of playing pieces

STEPPING STONES
The winning positions

The Game

This is a two-person strategy game played with a set of a monomino, domino, and tromino for each player. Players take turns placing their shapes on a 4-by-4 gameboard in sequence: first the monomino, then the domino, then the tromino. When all the pieces have been placed, successive moves follow the same order. The winner of the game is the first player who succeeds in creating a staircase configuration of his or her color, which can be in any orientation on the gameboard. A player must make a move on every turn and a player must not pass or replace a piece in the same position. It is also illegal to make a move which makes it impossible for the other player to move.

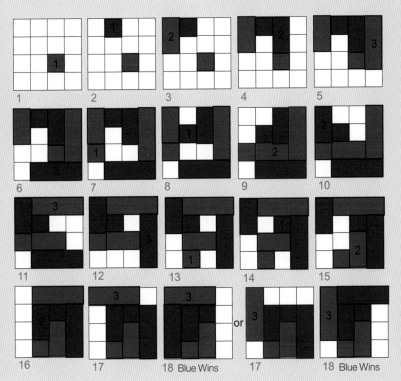

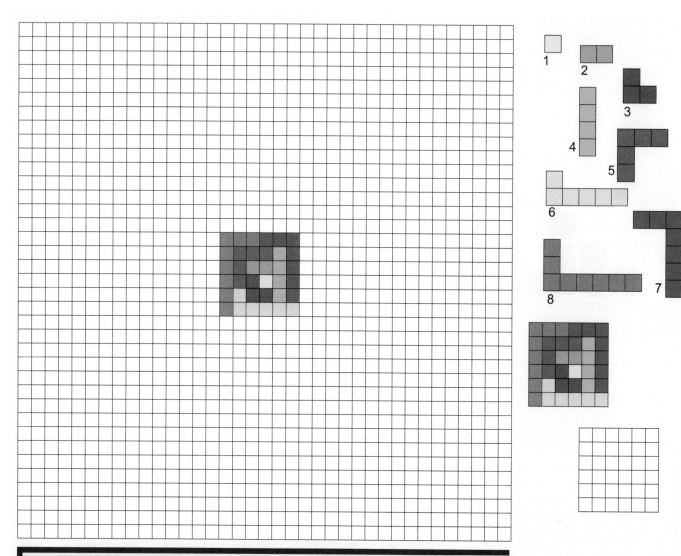

CONSECUTIVE POLYOMINO SPIRAL SQUARES

We can see that by choosing a special selection of consecutive polyominos, starting with a monomino in the center and adding to it a domino and further selected polyominos (one of each group), counterclockwise spiral configurations can be formed as shown. The first eight consecutive polyominos are shown, forming a polyomino spiral tessellating a six-by-six solid square.

Related to this construction principle, further interesting questions and problems can be posed:

1. Can you rearrange the pieces of the six-by-six square into other distinct patterns?

2. Continuing the formation of the spiral selecting the consecutive polyominos, at what stage will the next rectangle be formed, and what will be its proportions?

3. At what stage will the next square be formed and what will be its size?

026 8

40

OVERLAPPING TESSELLATION

Each of the intricate colored tessellations above, in which many irregular triangles, pentagons, hexagons, heptagons, and octagons can be found, was created from one single element. Can you tell what this element is in each case?

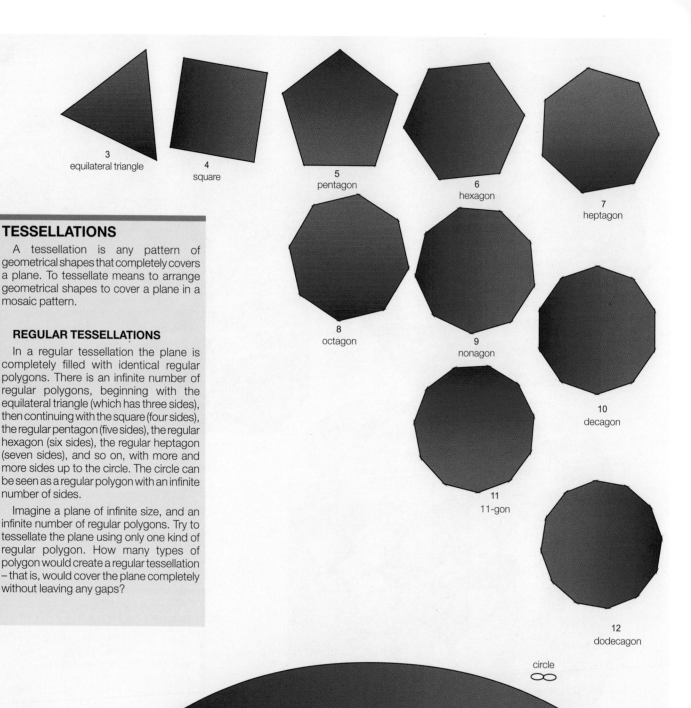

3
equilateral triangle

4
square

5
pentagon

6
hexagon

7
heptagon

8
octagon

9
nonagon

10
decagon

11
11-gon

12
dodecagon

circle

TESSELLATIONS

A tessellation is any pattern of geometrical shapes that completely covers a plane. To tessellate means to arrange geometrical shapes to cover a plane in a mosaic pattern.

REGULAR TESSELLATIONS

In a regular tessellation the plane is completely filled with identical regular polygons. There is an infinite number of regular polygons, beginning with the equilateral triangle (which has three sides), then continuing with the square (four sides), the regular pentagon (five sides), the regular hexagon (six sides), the regular heptagon (seven sides), and so on, with more and more sides up to the circle. The circle can be seen as a regular polygon with an infinite number of sides.

Imagine a plane of infinite size, and an infinite number of regular polygons. Try to tessellate the plane using only one kind of regular polygon. How many types of polygon would create a regular tessellation – that is, would cover the plane completely without leaving any gaps?

028 5

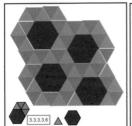
3.3.3.3.6

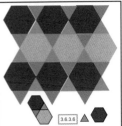
3.6.3.6

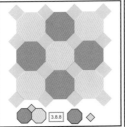
3.8.8

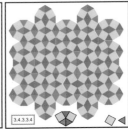
3.4.3.3.4

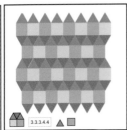
3.3.3.4.4

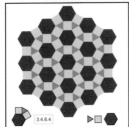
3.4.6.4

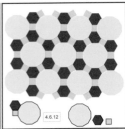
4.6.12

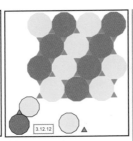
3.12.12

SEMI-REGULAR TESSELLATIONS

Semi-regular tessellations are those in which two or more kinds of regular polygon are fitted together to cover a plane in such a way that the same polygons, in the same cyclic order, surround every vertex (corner point) – or, in mathematical language, every vertex is congruent to every other vertex.

There are eight semi-regular tessellations, as shown. They are made up of only five different regular polygons: triangles, squares, hexagons, octagons and dodecagons. Tessellations of regular polygons with more than three different vertex pictures are infinite in number.

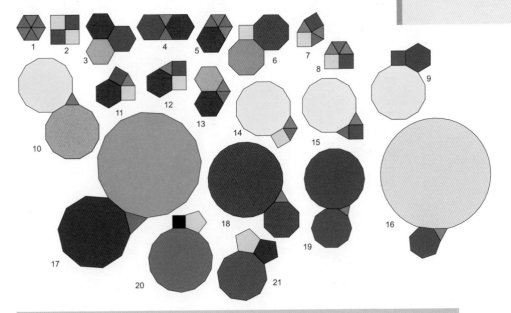

VERTEX PICTURES

The following polygons can create 21 vertex pictures, expressed by Schlafli symbols:

1- 3.3.3.3.3.3
2- 4.4.4.4
3- 6.6.6
4- 3.6.3.6
5- 3.3.3.3.6
6- 4.8.8
7- 3.4.3.3.4
8- 3.3.3.4.4
9- 4.6.12
10- 3.12.12
11- 3.4.6.4
12- 3.4.4.6
13- 3.3.6.6
14- 3.3.4.12
15- 3.4.3.12
16- 3.7.42
17- 3.9.18
18- 3.8.24
19- 3.10.15
20- 4.5.20
21- 5.5.10

OTHER TESSELLATIONS

If we omit the uniformity restriction that every vertex must look the same as every other, we can create an additional group of at least 14 demi-regular polyhedra, using combinations of two or three different polygon arrangements of vertex pictures, determined by a process of trial and error.

Tessellations of regular polygons with more than three different vertex pictures are infinite in number.

PINWHEEL PATTERNS AND TRIANGLES

A pattern in a plane has a symmetry of scale or is scalable if the tiles that make up the pattern can be grouped into "super-tiles" that cover the plane and, when scaled down, coincide with the original pattern. Square patterns and patterns of equilateral triangles are examples.

A rigid symmetry of the pattern in a plane is a motion of the plane that preserves the pattern without changing or distorting it. A rigid symmetry could be a motion of a part of the pattern by a translation, rotation, flip, or any combination of these.

Suppose we have a pattern that has symmetry of scale. Must that pattern also have rigid symmetries? The answer is no.

In the 1960s American mathematician Robert Berger constructed patterns that had no rigid symmetries and yet had symmetry of scale. His examples used thousands of tiles. In the 1970s British mathematician Roger Penrose discovered patterns that had no rigid symmetries and used only two tiles, which Penrose called "kites" and "darts." The two tiles could occur in one of ten possible orientations in a pattern. These became known as "Penrose patterns."

In 1994, John Conway of Princeton University and Charles Radin of the University of Texas discovered another tiling: the pinwheel pattern that uses only one single triangular tile. This tile can occur in an infinite number of orientations in a pinwheel pattern.

PINWHEEL TRIANGLES AND SUPER-TILING

For a pattern to have a symmetry of scale, the basic requirement is to be able to group the tiles into super-tiles of the same shape as the original, but larger. For the creation of pinwheel patterns the basic shape is the pinwheel triangle, a right-angled triangle with legs of lengths 1 and 2 units. Five such triangles form a super-tile called a five-unit pinwheel triangle.

There is only one way of grouping the pinwheel triangles into super-tiles in order to create a pinwheel pattern in the plane, shown above. Can you make a 125-unit pinwheel triangle, or even a 625-unit triangle?

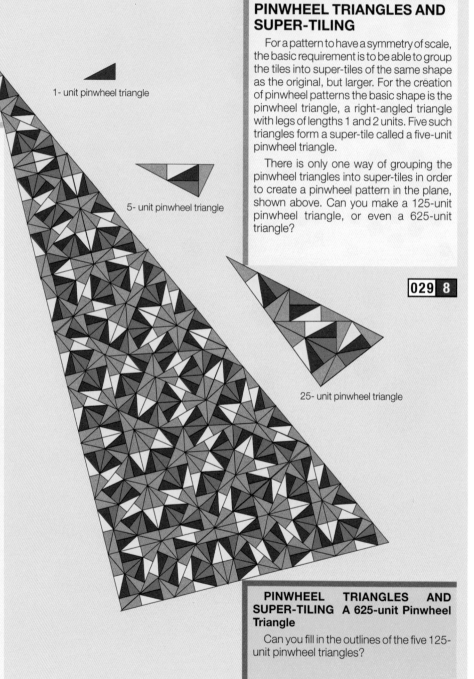

1- unit pinwheel triangle

5- unit pinwheel triangle

25- unit pinwheel triangle

029 8

PINWHEEL TRIANGLES AND SUPER-TILING A 625-unit Pinwheel Triangle

Can you fill in the outlines of the five 125-unit pinwheel triangles?

"Mathematics is the queen of science, and number theory is the queen of Mathematics."

Carl Friedrich Gauss

GAUSS COUNTING

The story of ten-year-old Gauss figuring out the sum of the first 100 counting numbers became a classic tale retold an endless number of times.

How long will it take you to add up all the numbers from 1 to 100?

1+2+3+4+5+6+7+8+9+10+11+12+13+14+15+16+17+18+19+20+21+22+23+24+25+26+27+28+29+30+31+32+33+34+35+36+37 +38+39+40+41+42+43+44+45+46+47+48+49+50+51+52+53+54+55+56+57+58+59+60+61+62+63+64+65+66+67+68+69+70+71+ 72+73+74+75+76+77+78+79+80+81+82+83+84+85+86+87+88+89+90+91+ 92+93+94+95+96+97+98+99+100 = ?

When the famous German mathematician Carl Friedrich Gauss (1777–1855) was ten, his teacher asked the class to add up the first 100 consecutive numbers. The teacher's assumption was that this would allow him some quiet time for himself and that he could forget about the class for a while. It must have surprised him that in just seconds he got the answer from Gauss. Young Gauss spotted the pattern behind the sequence of numbers and could provide the answer in no time, without even using a pencil and paper. Can you?

FIGURATE NUMBERS
Numbers as patterns

When numbers are represented by dots and arranged to form geometrical figures and patterns, meaningful relationships can be discovered. In this form they are called "polygonal numbers" or "figurate numbers."

Ancient Greek arithmetic was mainly occupied with studying figurate numbers, and their use led to the study of number series. Pythagoreans (followers of the 6th-century BCE mathematician Pythagoras) attached magical properties to figurate numbers.

Figurate numbers provide intuitive insights into aspects of elementary number theory and theory of games. The geometric visual representation of figurate numbers in many cases is so simple and beautiful that the proof of a theorem can be seen and understood at a single glance. The proof for the sum of the first n natural numbers is visualized by "triangular numbers;" the sum of consecutive odd integers is seen by "square numbers" – and so on.

The 100-th triangular number

How many dots, how long will it take you to count them? Young Gauss did it in seconds. (see: previous page/Gauss counting)

031 6

TRIANGULAR NUMBERS

Triangular numbers can be found by stacking a group of objects in a triangular fashion – two objects are placed after one, three objects after two, and so on. The fourth triangular number, for example is 10: $1 + 2 + 3 + 4 = 10$, as shown.

What is so special about triangular numbers is that they represent the sum of any number of consecutive integers. You won't have much difficulty in counting the tenth triangular number (55), as visualized below, but how long will it take you to find the hundredth triangular number, also visualized at bottom and next page?

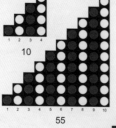

10

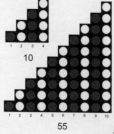

55

46

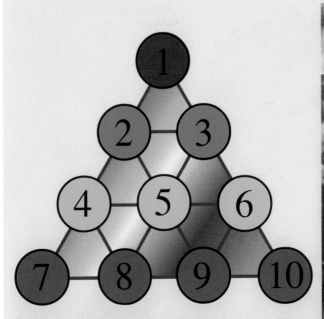

DIVINE TETRAKTYS

The fourth triangular number is composed of 10 points, the sum of the first consecutive integers, arranged in the shape of a pyramid, called the Tetraktys. It was devised by Pythagoras as a symbol of the creation of the known universe, and used as a sacred basis of the Pythagoreans' oath. The dots represent numbers from 1 to 10, the rows representing dimensions and the organization of space.

First row: a point – **zero dimension**.

Second row: a line of two points – **one dimension**.

Third row: a plane defined by a triangle of three points – **two dimensions**.

Fourth row: a tetrahedron defined by 4 points – **three dimensions**.

The last row also symbolizes the four elements: earth, air, fire, and water.

The Tetraktys is a beautiful symbol, representing the evolution from simplicity to complexity, and the abstract to the concrete. The Kabbalistic *Tree of Life* was later derived from the Tetraktys.

PYTHAGORAS BY RAPHAEL

Pythagoras is depicted demonstrating his theory of numbers to his disciples. The triangular numbers – which he considered the "best" numbers – and specifically the "best" of all these, the "Divine Tetraktys" 1 + 2 + 3 + 4 are shown on the tablet at the bottom.

The School of Athens by Raphael

032 10

THE COMBINATORIAL POWER OF TETRAKTYS

Can you give an intelligent guess as to how many different ways there are to place the ten numbers in the Tetraktys, not counting reflections and rotations?

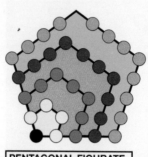

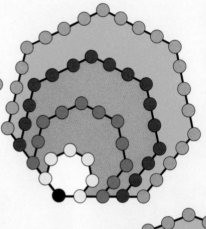

The first five heptagonal
numbers are visualized.
First 1
Second 7
Third 18
Fourth 34
Fifth 55
Sixth?
Can you determine the sixth
heptagonal number?

PENTAGONAL FIGURATE
NUMBERS
The first five pentagonal
numbers are visualized.
First 1
Second 5
Third 12
Fourth 22
Fifth 35
Sixth?
Can you determine the sixth
pentagonal number?

HEXAGONAL FIGURATE
NUMBERS
The first five hexagonal
numbers are visualized.
First 1
Second 6
Third 15
Fourth 28
Fifth 45
Sixth?
Can you determine the sixth
hexagonal number?

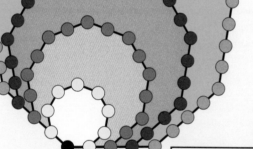

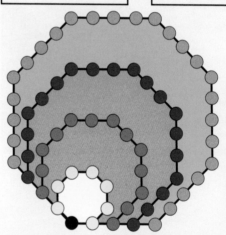

OCTAGONAL FIGURATE
NUMBERS
The first five octagonal
numbers are visualized.
First 1
Second 8
Third 21
Fourth 40
Fifth 65
Sixth?
Can you determine the sixth
octagonal number?

NONAGONAL FIGURATE
NUMBERS
The first five nonagonal
numbers are visualized.
First 1
Second 9
Third 24
Fourth 46
Fifth 75
Sixth?
Can you determine the sixth
nonagonal number?

POLYGONAL FIGURATE NUMBERS

Figurate numbers can be triangular or square, as we have seen, but can also be extended into polygonal forms. A polygonal number is a number composed of dots arranged in the pattern of a regular polygon such as a pentagon or hexagon.

Ancient mathematicians probably developed polygonal figurate numbers using pebbles or other simple counters as a way of investigating the relationships between numbers. The invention of the abacus evolved from such beginnings and became a powerful tool in early mathematics.

Here we demonstrate a few polygonal figurate number series. When calculating the totals, you include the dots of previous polygons in the series; you don't just count the dots in the next largest shape. So, for example, the third pentagonal number is 12 because it is the number of orange and yellow and black dots in total. This is a very interesting area to explore further, for there are many surprising discoveries and complex relationships between these numbers.

1 =	
2 =	not possible
3 =	1 + 2
4 =	
5 =	
6 =	
7 =	
8 =	
9 =	
10 =	
11 =	
12 =	
13 =	
14 =	
15 =	
16 =	
17 =	
18 =	
19 =	
20 =	
21 =	
22 =	
23 =	
24 =	
25 =	

26 =
27 =
28 =
29 =
30 =
31 =
32 =
33 =
34 =
35 =
36 =
37 =
38 =
39 =
40 =
41 =
....

CONSECUTIVE INTEGERS

Here is a list of the first 41 consecutive integers. Which of them can't be expressed as a sum of consecutive integers? Is there a general rule to find these numbers easily?

UNIQUE NUMBERS

If a number of n consecutive digits in ascending order is subtracted from the number obtained by reversing the digits of the initial number, the result is the "unique number" or U_n.

For example, if the two-digit number 23 is subtracted from its reverse, 32, the result is:

| 2 | 3 | | 3 | 2 | | 2 | 3 | = | 9 | is the unique **number** U_n

How long will it take you to find the unique numbers for the following list of three-, four-, five-, six-, and seven-digit consecutive numbers? It took me less than a minute. How did I do it?

Three-digit	Unique number
123	
234	
345	
456	
567	
678	
789	

Four-digit	Unique number
1234	
2345	
3456	
4567	
5678	
6789	

Five-digit	Unique number
12345	
23456	
34567	
45678	
56789	

Six-digit	Unique number
123456	
234567	
345678	
456789	

Seven-digit	Unique number
1234567	
2345678	
3456789	

035 6

50

THINK OF A NUMBER.
ADD 10.
DOUBLE THE RESULT.
SUBTRACT 6.
DIVIDE BY 2 AND TAKE AWAY THE NUMBER
YOU ORIGINALLY THOUGHT OF.
THE RESULT WILL ALWAYS BE 7.
WHY?

THINK OF A NUMBER

Or, the significance of the mathematical proof

In recreational mathematics there are many different variations of the "think of a number" problem. But why and how does the trick work?

You can, of course, check the results by several specific choices of numbers, and see that each time the trick will work. However, not every one of these will give you the answer of how it works and provide the proof that it will always work, no matter what number you think of. So what will? A mathematical proof – if only we have the right IDEA how to deal with the problem.

THINK OF A NUMBER – AGAIN!

Think of a number from 1 to 10.
Multiply that number by 9.
If the number is a two-digit number, add the digits together.
Now subtract 5.

Determine which letter in the alphabet corresponds to the number you ended up with:
1-2-3-4-5-6-7-8-9-10-11-12-13-14-15-16-17-18-19-20-21-22-23-24-25-26
a-b-c-d-e-f- g-h -i - j - k - l - m - n - o - p-q - r - s - t - u - v - w - x - y - z

Think of a country that starts with that letter.
Remember the last letter of the name of that country.

Think of a name of an animal that starts with that letter.
Remember the last letter in the name of that animal.

Think of a name of a fruit that starts with that letter.
Check your result with mine in the solution part.

LOVELY NUMBER 1089

Select any three-digit number in which the three digits are different and follow the instructions.

We have selected 825 **Your choice:**

(1) Reverse the digits 528 **Your choice:**

(2) Subtract the two numbers

$$8\ 2\ 5 - 5\ 2\ 8 = 2\ 9\ 7$$

Your choice: ☐☐☐ – ☐☐☐ = ☐☐☐

(3) Take the difference, reverse its digits and add the two numbers together:

$$2\ 9\ 7 + 7\ 9\ 2 = 1\ 0\ 8\ 9$$

Your choice: ☐☐☐ + ☐☐☐ = 1 0 8 9

Note that when you reverse the digits at this stage, you need to include any leading zero. (For example, if your initial number was 102, you'd end up with 99 at the end of step 2. You would need to write this as 099 then reverse it as 990.)

Amazingly, your choice produced the same number we predicted.

Try another number. You will be even more astonished that no matter which number you select it will always end with **1089**.

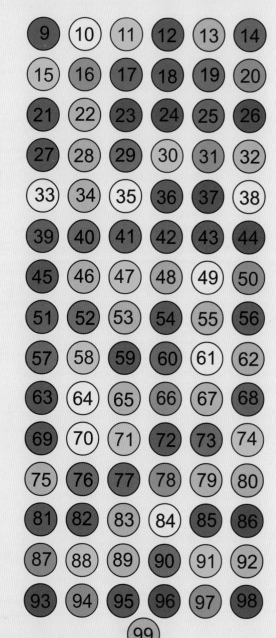

TELEPATHIC NUMBER MAGIC

Look at the number pattern (right). Starting from 9, it incorporates the first 90 two-digit numbers, and each number is associated with one of seven colors. I shall use my telepathic powers to influence your choice of numbers so that the outcome of your choice will always be a blue number.

Pick any of the two-digit numbers, add up the two digits, and then subtract that sum from your chosen number. No matter what your initial numbers was, the result will always be a blue number.

If you believe in telepathy you will be impressed.

But if not, can you discover the secret of my "telepathic powers"?

EARRINGS

At the ball there were 900 women.

2 per cent were wearing one earring.

50 per cent of the rest were wearing two earrings, while the other half were wearing none.

How many earrings were at the ball?

55

1	11	21	31	41	51	61	71	81	91
2	12	22	32	42	52	62	72	82	92
3	13	23	33	43	53	63	73	83	93
4	14	24	34	44	54	64	74	84	94
5	15	25	35	45	55	65	75	85	95
6	16	26	36	46	56	66	76	86	96
7	17	27	37	47	57	67	77	87	97
8	18	28	38	48	58	68	78	88	98
9	19	29	39	49	59	69	79	89	99
10	20	30	40	50	60	70	80	90	100

$$10 - 10\%$$

$$100 - 19\%$$

$$1000 - \text{?}$$

$$10^{64} - \text{?}$$

1	11	21	31	41	51	61	71	81	91
2	12	22	32	42	52	62	72	82	92
3	13	23	33	43	53	63	73	83	93
4	14	24	34	44	54	64	74	84	94
5	15	25	35	45	55	65	75	85	95
6	16	26	36	46	56	66	76	86	96
7	17	27	37	47	57	67	77	87	97
8	18	28	38	48	58	68	78	88	98
9	19	29	39	49	59	69	79	89	99
10	20	30	40	50	60	70	80	90	100

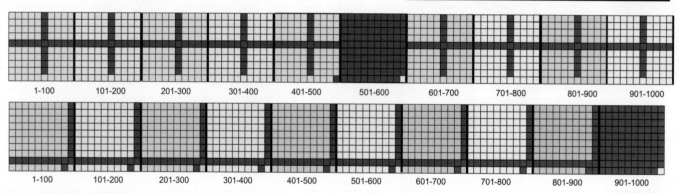

1-100 101-200 201-300 301-400 401-500 501-600 601-700 701-800 801-900 901-1000

1-100 101-200 201-300 301-400 401-500 501-600 601-700 701-800 801-900 901-1000

ALL FIVES PARADOX

041 5

How many times does the digit 5 appear in 1000 numbers? You may be surprised by the result.

In the first 10 numbers, the digit 5 appears in only one of them (10 per cent).

Of the first 100 numbers (10^2), as we can see, 19 numbers have a 5 in them, about one-fifth or 19 per cent.

How will this proportion change for the first 1000 numbers (10^3) shown above?

Can you make a guess – what will the percentage of numbers having a five in them be for a very, very large number,

let's say 10^{64}?

9999999999999999999999999999999999999999

23
+5
28
+10
38
+11
49
+13
62
+8
70
+7
77
+14
91
+10
101
+2
103
+4
107
+8
115
.....

KAPREKAR'S DIGITADDITION

Indian mathematician DR Kaprekar (1905–1986) was initially mocked by contemporaries who believed his games with numbers were trivial. Yet he made astonishing discoveries, which were revealed by Martin Gardner in the journal *Scientific American* and obtained world-wide recognition for Kaprekar. He became renowned for his contribution to recreational mathematics and number theory.

One of Kaprekar's discoveries was the process of "digitaddition."

Select a positive integer and add to it the sum of its digits.

Take 23. The process of digitaddition for this number is demonstrated.

23 + 5 = 28

23 is called a generator. The new number 28 is called a generated number.

The process can be repeated endlessly, forming a digitaddition series, as demonstrated:

28, 28, 38, 49, 62, 70, 77, 91, 101, 103, 107, **115**

No formula has been found for the partial sum of the series, given its first and last term, but I could perform an impressive magic feat.

Imagine we are together in a room. You select a number as a new generator and create a partial digitaddition series, as long as you wish. Tell me your number and the last number in the series. I shall tell you in a second the sum of all the digits in your digitaddition series. Impressive?

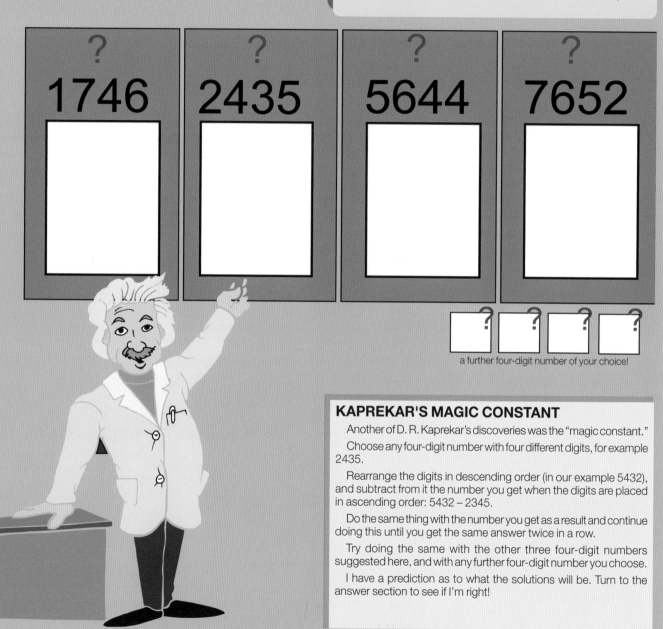

? 1746
? 2435
? 5644
? 7652

? ? ? ?

a further four-digit number of your choice!

KAPREKAR'S MAGIC CONSTANT

Another of D. R. Kaprekar's discoveries was the "magic constant."

Choose any four-digit number with four different digits, for example 2435.

Rearrange the digits in descending order (in our example 5432), and subtract from it the number you get when the digits are placed in ascending order: 5432 – 2345.

Do the same thing with the number you get as a result and continue doing this until you get the same answer twice in a row.

Try doing the same with the other three four-digit numbers suggested here, and with any further four-digit number you choose.

I have a prediction as to what the solutions will be. Turn to the answer section to see if I'm right!

COLLATZ NUMBER PROBLEM

In 1932, 20-year old German mathematics student Lothar Collatz discovered a strange outcome when dealing with a seemingly simple mathematical calculation.

The calculation is outlined below.

Take a positive integer x.

If it is even halve it: x/2.

If it is odd multiply it by 3, add 1, and then halve it: (3x + 1)/2.

Using these results, start all over again according to these rules and continue until you get number 1, which then produces a never-ending loop of 4,2,1...

Collatz was surprised to find that this happened every time he tried the calculation, and he wondered whether it would always do so. The Collatz problem named after him asks whether the sequences will *always* reach 1 for all integers.

In the accompanying table this is illustrated for the first ten integers, save 7. As we can see, in each case the sequence reaches 1 eventually, after which the endless loop of 4,2,1... is encountered.

The sequences produced by the Collatz problem are known as Hailstone numbers, because their values rise and fall like a hailstone from a cloud.

English mathematician John H. Conway proved that the Collatz problem is not decidable because it is neither formally provable or unprovable. Hungarian mathematician Paul Erdös noted, "Mathematics is not yet ready for such problems."

Today's super-computers have tested all numbers up to 27 quadrillion (27,000,000,000,000,000). Not one was found whose Hailstone sequence did not eventually end with 1. The longest Hailstone sequence worked out to date is a 15-digit number whose Hailstone sequence consists of 1,820 numbers.

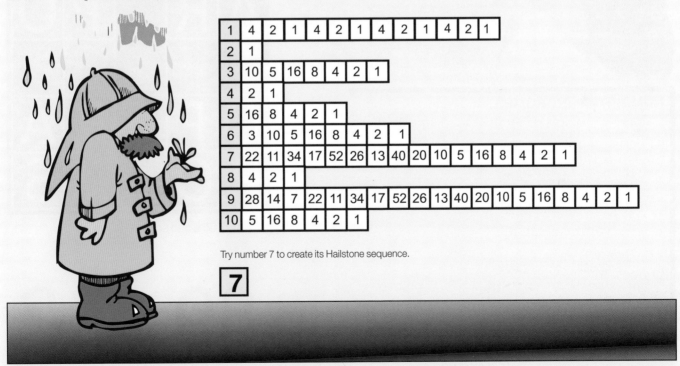

1	4	2	1	4	2	1	4	2	1	4	2	1						
2	1																	
3	10	5	16	8	4	2	1											
4	2	1																
5	16	8	4	2	1													
6	3	10	5	16	8	4	2	1										
7	22	11	34	17	52	26	13	40	20	10	5	16	8	4	2	1		
8	4	2	1															
9	28	14	7	22	11	34	17	52	26	13	40	20	10	5	16	8	4	2	1
10	5	16	8	4	2	1												

Try number 7 to create its Hailstone sequence.

7

PALINDROMES

A "palindrome" (from Greek words meaning "back" and "direction") is a word, sentence, number, or anything else that reads the same in either direction.

Palindromes date back at least to 79CE, when a palindromic word square was found as a graffito at Herculaneum, buried by the ash of the Vesuv that year with the sentence "SATOR AREPO TENET OPERA ROTAS."

The translation is problematic. Two possible translations are:
(1) "The sower Arepo holds the wheels with effort."
(2) "The sower Arepo leads with his hand on the plough."

NUMBER PALINDROMES

Take any positive number, reverse its digits, and add them to the original number. Repeat this procedure with the sum you get until you end up with a palindromic number, as we have done below with 234, 1924 and 5280:

```
   234        1924          5280
 + 432      + 4291        + 0825
   666        6215          6105

            + 5126        + 5016
             11341         11121
            +14311       + 12111
             25652         23232
```

Will every number ultimately produce a palindromic number with this procedure?

Try 89 and see how that goes!

PALINDROMIC WORD SQUARE (79 A.D.)

89.....?

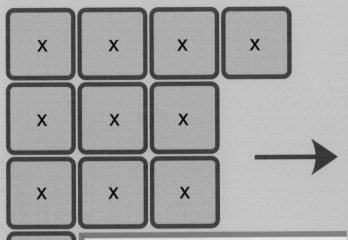

GENERAL'S ARRAYS

GENERAL'S ARRAY 1

In each of the 11 groups (red boxes), there is an identical number of soldiers x. If you

add their leader the General, the total number can be rearranged to form a single perfect square array of soldiers.

Can you work out the minimal number of soldiers in each group and the number of soldiers in the square array (including the General)?

y^2

GENERAL'S ARRAY 2

Another time the General wants to arrange his men into eight rows, with eight men in every row, so that he can place himself at a point equidistant from every row. How can you rearrange the eight rows of soldiers according to the General's orders?

HOTEL INFINITY

In mathematics the concept of infinity, while often paradoxical and contradictory, is profoundly meaningful.

Paradoxes devised by Ancient Greek mathematicians such as Zeno of Elea (c.450CE) showed that infinity could not be ignored. One of Zeno's most famous paradoxes concerned a race between Achilles and a tortoise in which Achilles gave the tortoise a head start: on an imaginary line between Achilles and the tortoise there would be an infinite number of points that Achilles had not yet reached and where the tortoise had already been, so that in theory Achilles could never overtake the tortoise.

For more than 2,000 years after the time of the Ancient Greeks, mathematicians were unsure what to make of the concept of the infinite. The first mathematician to suggest that reason could somehow be applied to infinity without being entirely contradictory was German cardinal Nicholas of Cusa (1401–1464). He taught that in the infinite, the circle coincides with the line. He also said that all we can know about the infinite is that we cannot know the infinite; we must understand it through the coincidence of opposites.

In the 1870s German mathematician Georg Cantor (1845-1918) created transfinite mathematics, a new branch of mathematics that seemingly resolved all the mysteries and puzzles posed by the infinite. Cantor used set theory and the idea of cardinality to prove the existence of the infinite and also of different orders of infinity.

In mathematics any collection of things is called a set. Two sets have the same cardinality if there is a one-to-one correspondence between their numbers. These two very simple principles lead to quite paradoxical conclusions.

The first, and the strangest, is that there are different sizes of infinity – a very counterintuitive idea. Consider the set of even numbers. Obviously, there are only half as many of them as there are integers, but the two sets have the same cardinality, because there is a one-to-one correspondence between their numbers (each even number 2n corresponds to the integer n). The sets are of different sizes but both are infinite.

The set of rational numbers (numbers in the form of a/b, where a and b are integers) appears to contain far more numbers than the set of integers since there is an infinite number of rationals between every pair of integers: 1, 2, 3, 4, 5..., yet the two sets have the same cardinality.

Centuries earlier, Italian mathematician Galileo (1564–1642) called attention to the paradoxical concept of the one-to-one correspondence between counting numbers and their squares:

1 2 3 4 5 6 7 8....
1 4 9 16 25 36 49 64.....

even though, intuitively, there seemed to be fewer squares than counting numbers.

HOTEL INFINITY

Hotel Infinity has an infinite number of rooms. No matter how full the hotel is, there is always room for the next arrival. The manager simply moves the person in room 1 into room 2, the person in room 2 into room 3, and so on. At the end of the process, which may take some time, room number 1 becomes vacant for the new guest. But how can the hotel manager cope with the problem of accommodating an infinite number of guests arriving at once?

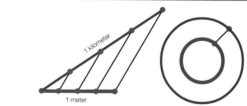

THE ONE-TO-ONE CORRESPONDENCE PARADOX

There is the same number of points on a line of 1 millimeter, 1 meter, or 1 kilometer in length! The points along the two circles can be paired up in a one-to-one correspondence so they must have the same number of points as well.

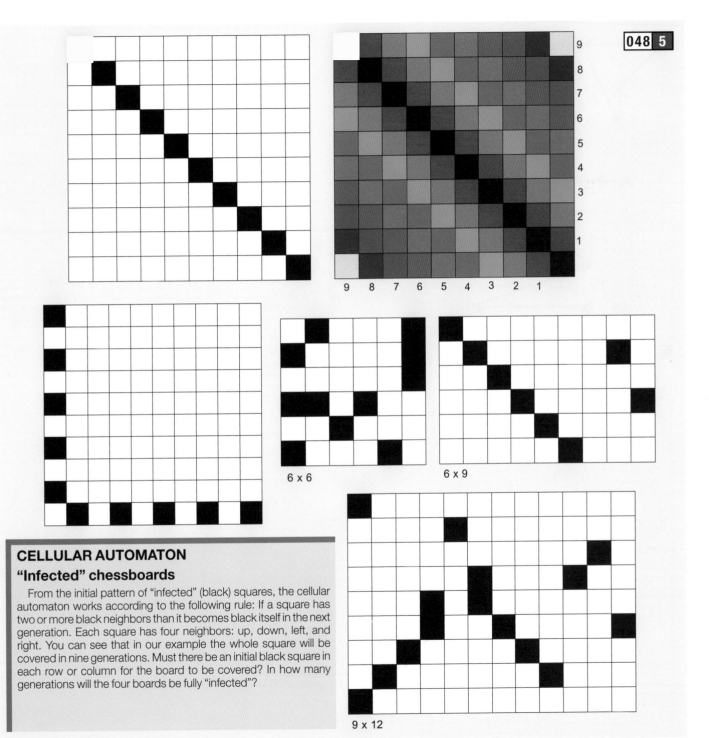

CELLULAR AUTOMATON
"Infected" chessboards

From the initial pattern of "infected" (black) squares, the cellular automaton works according to the following rule: If a square has two or more black neighbors than it becomes black itself in the next generation. Each square has four neighbors: up, down, left, and right. You can see that in our example the whole square will be covered in nine generations. Must there be an initial black square in each row or column for the board to be covered? In how many generations will the four boards be fully "infected"?

6 x 6

6 x 9

9 x 12

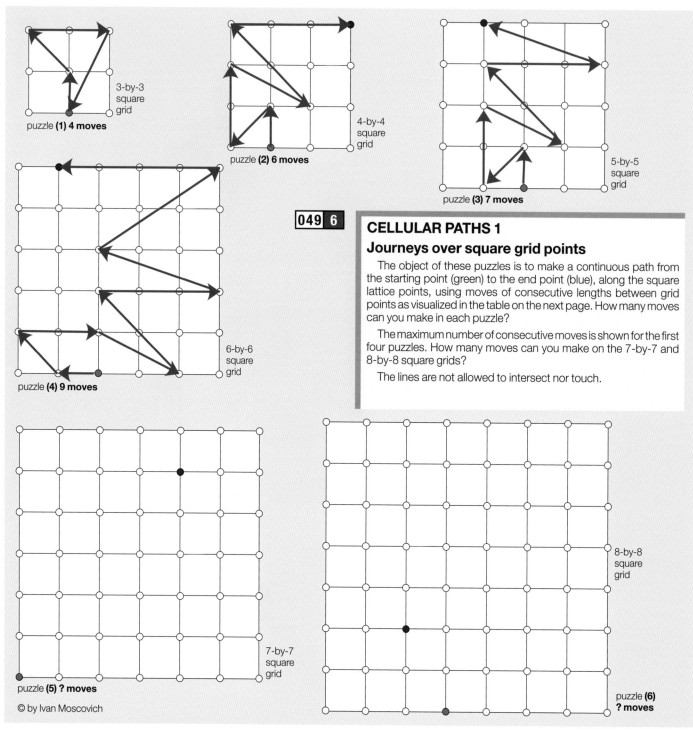

puzzle **(1) 4 moves**

3-by-3 square grid

puzzle **(2) 6 moves**

4-by-4 square grid

puzzle **(3) 7 moves**

5-by-5 square grid

puzzle **(4) 9 moves**

6-by-6 square grid

CELLULAR PATHS 1
Journeys over square grid points

The object of these puzzles is to make a continuous path from the starting point (green) to the end point (blue), along the square lattice points, using moves of consecutive lengths between grid points as visualized in the table on the next page. How many moves can you make in each puzzle?

The maximum number of consecutive moves is shown for the first four puzzles. How many moves can you make on the 7-by-7 and 8-by-8 square grids?

The lines are not allowed to intersect nor touch.

puzzle **(5) ? moves**

7-by-7 square grid

8-by-8 square grid

puzzle **(6) ? moves**

© by Ivan Moscovich

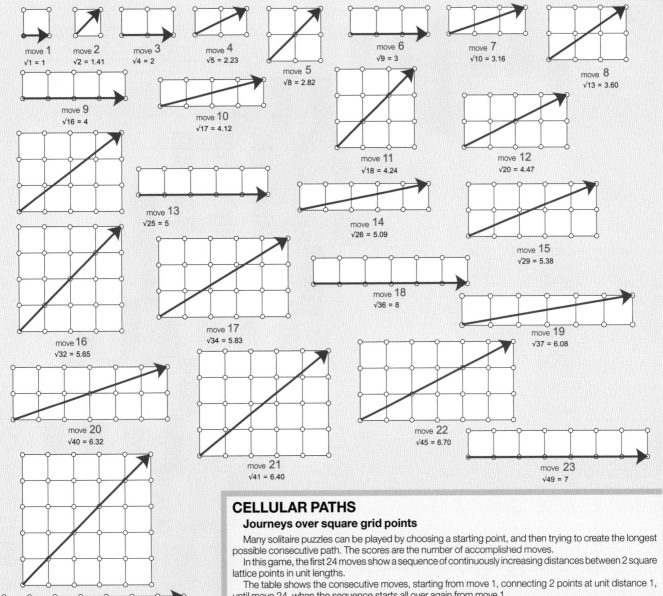

move 1
√1 = 1

move 2
√2 = 1.41

move 3
√4 = 2

move 4
√5 = 2.23

move 5
√8 = 2.82

move 6
√9 = 3

move 7
√10 = 3.16

move 8
√13 = 3.60

move 9
√16 = 4

move 10
√17 = 4.12

move 11
√18 = 4.24

move 12
√20 = 4.47

move 13
√25 = 5

move 14
√26 = 5.09

move 15
√29 = 5.38

move 16
√32 = 5.65

move 17
√34 = 5.83

move 18
√36 = 8

move 19
√37 = 6.08

move 20
√40 = 6.32

move 21
√41 = 6.40

move 22
√45 = 6.70

move 23
√49 = 7

move 24
√50 = 7.07

CELLULAR PATHS

Journeys over square grid points

Many solitaire puzzles can be played by choosing a starting point, and then trying to create the longest possible consecutive path. The scores are the number of accomplished moves.

In this game, the first 24 moves show a sequence of continuously increasing distances between 2 square lattice points in unit lengths.

The table shows the consecutive moves, starting from move 1, connecting 2 points at unit distance 1, until move 24, when the sequence starts all over again from move 1.

The paper-and-pencil puzzle games based on this sequence are played on a gameboard with a square grid of 15-by-15 unit squares.

In 2-person competition games, players choose a starting point and compete, or follow the objectives on numbered puzzles.

The lines are not allowed to intersect nor touch.

You can see that at moves 13 and 24, players have the choice between two possible moves of the same lengths.

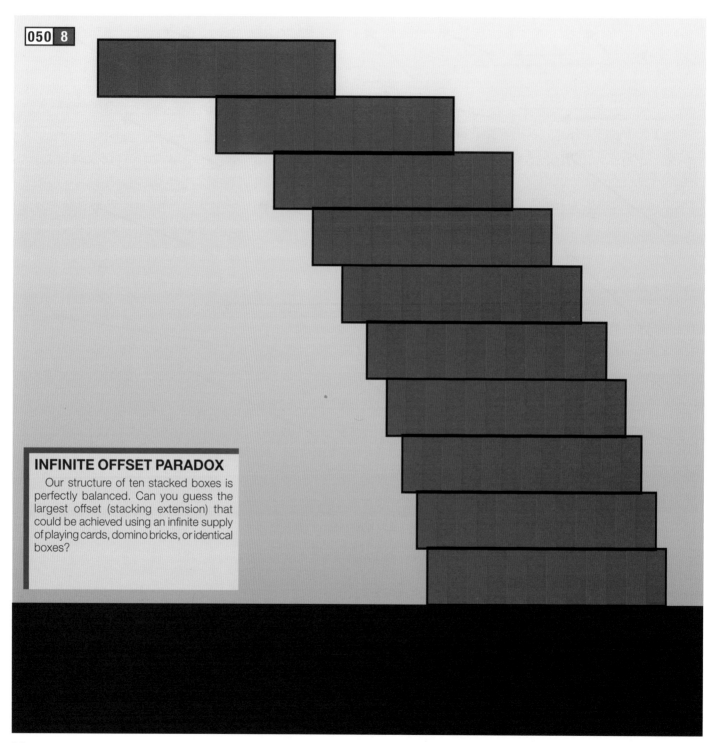

INFINITE OFFSET PARADOX

Our structure of ten stacked boxes is perfectly balanced. Can you guess the largest offset (stacking extension) that could be achieved using an infinite supply of playing cards, domino bricks, or identical boxes?

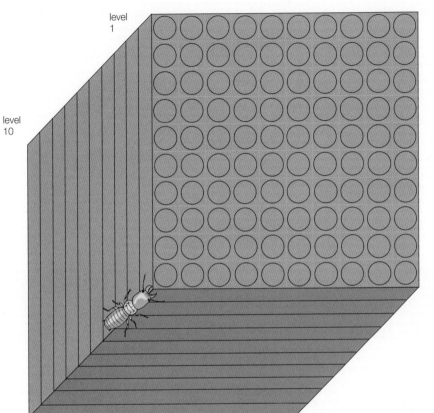

MYSTERY CUBE WALK

A 3-D cellular walk in a 10-by-10-by-10 cube

The cube with sides of 10 units has 10 layers. It is attacked by a woodworm, which starts its walk in the top layer's bottom-left cell. Its moves follow the consecutive sequence of 1 to 9 cells, always at right angles to the previous move in straight lines, up-down, left-right. No intersection of moves is allowed.

When the maximum number of consecutive moves is reached in a level, the moves start all over again from 1. When no further moves are possible the walk goes down to the next level and continues from the move reached in previous level, and so on, until the last level is reached.

How many cells will the woodworm have eaten by the end of the last level? The walk on level one is shown.

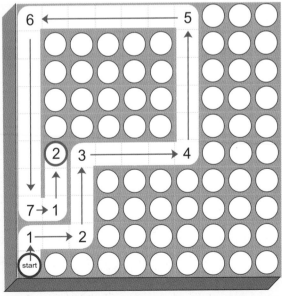

level 1

67

PRIME NUMBERS
THE MUSIC OF THE PRIMES

Prime numbers are whole numbers that can be divided only by 1 and themselves. They are the building blocks of integers. Their basic importance to mathematics is that all other numbers can be built up from primes.

Every number is either a prime or a composite that can be written as a product of smaller primes in a unique way. It appears to be true that every even number greater than 2 can be written as the sum of two primes – but this remains a theory, known as Goldbach's Conjecture, since it has not yet been mathematically proven for all cases. We do know for sure, however, that every odd number greater than 9 can be written as the sum of three primes – this has been proven by Vinogradoff's Proof. Goldbach's Conjecture was first proposed in 1742 by Prussian mathematician Christian Goldbach (1690–1764). Vinogradov's Proof was devised by Russian mathematician Ivan Vinogradov (1891–1983).

Determining whether a number is a prime or composite is a kind of game for mathematicians all over the world. Yet despite their apparent simplicity, prime numbers remain the most mysterious objects studied by mathematicians.

In the quest for order and pattern, primes are the ultimate challenge. Some mathematicians think that behind the primes is the secret of creation, of everything.

There is no formula for primes. The only known method of preparing a list of prime numbers up to a given limit is to write down all the integers and in a systematic way eliminate all the composite integers to leave the primes. This is known as the Sieve of Eratosthenes after the Ancient Greek mathematician, geographer and astronomer of that name (276–194BCE).

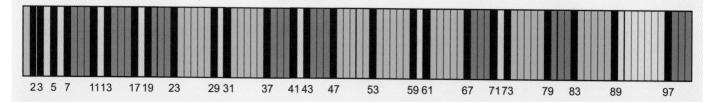

2 3 5 7 11 13 17 19 23 29 31 37 41 43 47 53 59 61 67 71 73 79 83 89 97

PRIME NUMBERS UP TO 100

Look through a list of prime numbers up to 100. Their distribution seems random. There is no pattern to determine the next prime. There are 25 primes among the first 100 numbers. What is their distribution in the next 100 numbers?

The central difficulty is that primes are scattered along the series of integers in a pattern that defies all attempts at precise description. In the 19th century German mathematician Bernhard Riemann (1826–66) looked at the problem of primes in a completely new way. He suggested that underlying the outward randomness of the primes is a subtle inner harmony. His bold prediction of the existence of this harmony, known as the Riemann Hypothesis, still awaits proof and explanation.

052 8

The many astonishing and still unsolved characteristics of prime numbers have fascinated mathematicians since the time of Ancient Greek mathematician Euclid (323-283BCE). Some of these are as follows.

(1) Is there a largest prime or do they go on forever?

(2) Can every number greater than 1 be expressed as a product of primes in one unique way?

(3) Primes are becoming rarer the farther we look. How big can the distance become between two numbers not including a prime? Can you for instance, find an interval of 1000 numbers (or any other number you choose) without a single prime?

(4) Is there always at least one prime between any number and its double?

(5) Do prime twins k and k+2 go on forever like the primes themselves?

(6) One of the latest exciting discoveries concerning prime numbers was incidental. If the integers are placed in the form of a counter-clockwise spiral, moving out from the center, the primes seem to have an uncanny tendency to appear into straight lines.

"It will be another million years, at least, before we understand the primes."

Hungarian mathematician Paul Erdös (1913–96)

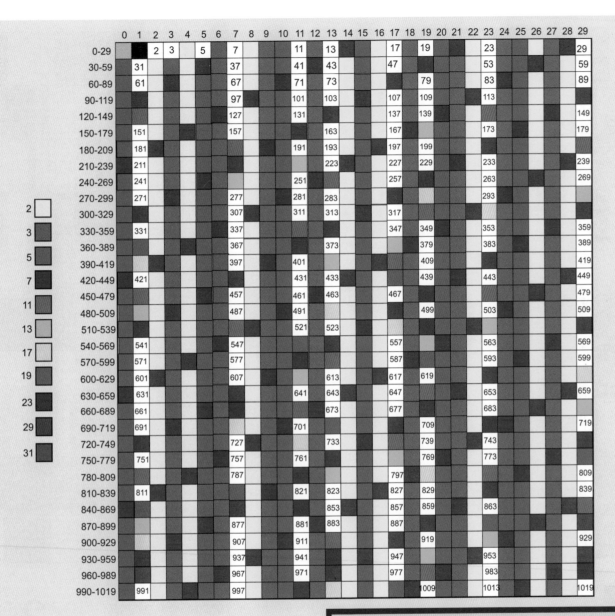

SIEVE OF ERATOSTHENES

How many primes are there in the first 1019 numbers?

After all the composite numbers are eliminated, there are 171 primes left as shown.

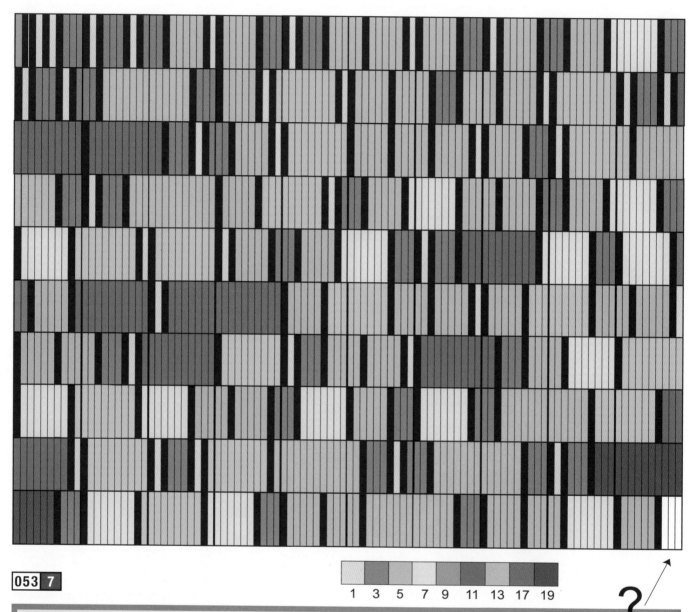

053 7

| 1 | 3 | 5 | 7 | 9 | 11 | 13 | 17 | 19 |

?

THE PATTERN OF THE PRIMES
MUSIC OF THE PRIMES

Here you can see the distribution pattern of Prime numbers from 1 to 1000.

Can you work out what will be the color at the end of the table to complete the color pattern?

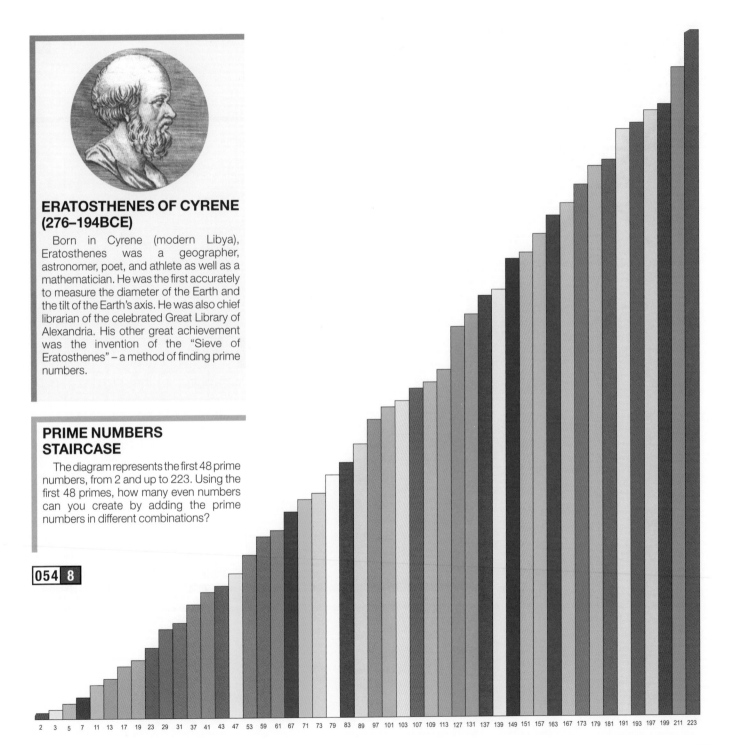

ERATOSTHENES OF CYRENE (276–194BCE)

Born in Cyrene (modern Libya), Eratosthenes was a geographer, astronomer, poet, and athlete as well as a mathematician. He was the first accurately to measure the diameter of the Earth and the tilt of the Earth's axis. He was also chief librarian of the celebrated Great Library of Alexandria. His other great achievement was the invention of the "Sieve of Eratosthenes" – a method of finding prime numbers.

PRIME NUMBERS STAIRCASE

The diagram represents the first 48 prime numbers, from 2 and up to 223. Using the first 48 primes, how many even numbers can you create by adding the prime numbers in different combinations?

054 8

2 3 5 7 11 13 17 19 23 29 31 37 41 43 47 53 59 61 67 71 73 79 83 89 97 101 103 107 109 113 127 131 137 139 149 151 157 163 167 173 179 181 191 193 197 199 211 223

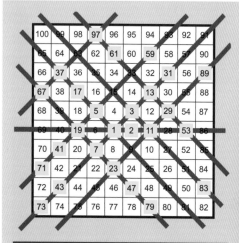

PRIME SPIRAL

In 1963 Polish mathematician Stanislaw Ulam (1909–84) was doodling numbers on a piece of paper during a boring lecture. He wrote down consecutive numbers in a square matrix, starting with 1 in the middle and spiraling outward as shown in our grid. To his utter surprise, prime numbers tended to fall on diagonal and straight lines.

As a matter of fact in his matrix the first 26 prime numbers all fall on straight lines containing at least 3 primes, while some diagonal lines contain even more primes. The same mysterious line patterns appear in larger matrices as well, charting millions of primes in a spiral pattern, all forming similar configurations.

Is this a law of nature – or just a coincidence? No one knows as yet.

213	212	211	210	209	208	207	206	205	204	203	202	201	200	199
214	161	160	159	158	157	156	155	154	153	152	151	150	149	198
215	162	117	116	115	114	113	112	111	110	109	108	107	148	197
216	163	118	81	80	79	78	77	76	75	74	73	106	147	196
217	164	119	82	53	52	51	50	49	48	47	72	105	146	195
218	165	120	83	54	33	32	31	30	29	46	71	104	145	194
219	166	121	84	55	34	21	20	19	28	45	70	103	144	193
220	167	122	85	56	35	22	17	18	27	44	69	102	143	192
221	168	123	86	57	36	23	24	25	26	43	68	101	142	191
222	169	124	87	58	37	38	39	40	41	42	67	100	141	190
223	170	125	88	59	60	61	62	63	64	65	66	99	140	189
224	171	126	89	90	91	92	93	94	95	96	97	98	139	188
225	172	127	128	129	130	131	132	133	134	135	136	137	138	187
226	173	174	175	176	177	178	179	180	181	182	183	184	185	186
227	228	229	230	231	232	233	234	235	236	237	238	239	240	241

Ulam also tried matrices that start from whole numbers other than 1, like the one shown above, which starts with 17 in the middle. He was astonished to observe strange patterns in the distribution of prime numbers in these spirals.

Shade in the primes as follows to see the pattern for yourself:

17, 19, 23, 29, 31, 37, 41, 43, 47, 53, 59, 61, 67, 71, 73, 79, 83, 89, 97,

101, 103, 107, 109, 113, 127, 131, 137, 139, 149, 151, 157, 163, 167, 173, 179, 181, 191, 193, 197, 199, 211, 223, 227, 229, 233, 239, 241.

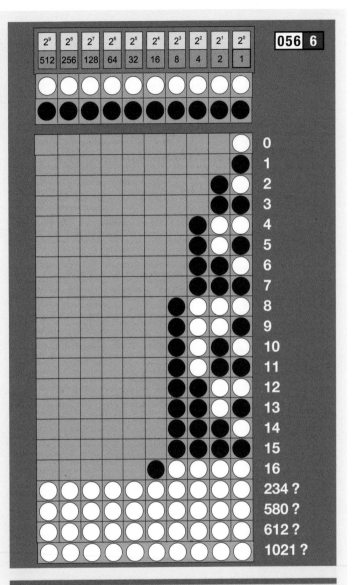

> "There are 10 types of people in this world. Those that understand the binary system and those that don't."
>
> *Anonymous*
>
> "Binary ... So simple, even a computer could do it."
>
> *Kerry Redshaw*

THE BINARY WORLD

The binary number system and the language of the computer

The simplest possible number system is the binary system based on the successive power of 2. In this system any number can be written using only 0s and 1s – for example, 2 is written 10 (one 2 and no units), 3 is 11 and 4 is 100. Some primitive tribes count in binary ways, and ancient Chinese mathematicians knew about the binary system, but the binary system was fully developed by the great German mathematician Gottfried von Leibniz (1646–1716) in his article *Explication de l'Arithmetique Binaire*.

To Leibniz the binary system symbolized a metaphysical truth. According to him, the entire world became possible by a binary split between being and nothingness: the universe is composed of and structured by the interdependent opposites of the physical (1) and nonphysical (0), and it is this binary pairing that provides the foundation of everything. Leibniz also believed that a purely mathematical approach to logic could be developed through his binary system by using 0 for false and 1 for true.

But the binary system of Leibniz was no more than a philosophical curiosity for hundreds of years until the advent of the computer. In 1854 British mathematician George Boole (1815–64) created a logical system, Boolean algebra, which was instrumental in implementing the binary system in electronic circuitry. In 1937 American mathematician and electronics engineer Claude Shannon (1916–2001) created a practical digital circuit design that enabled the development of the modern electronic computer.

A computer uses the binary system to perform all its functions. Its basic unit was originally the vacuum tube, then the transistor, then a chip. Its math is simple, as we can see from the binary abacus: we just count up to 1, starting each time from zero.

We live in a binary world today. The binary system of computers processes data coded in binary forms using a simple "on-off" switch. Computers operate at enormous speeds, and these on-off switches work at nanosecond speeds of 1,000,000,000 times per second.

BINARY ABACUS

The binary abacus operates on the same principle as the classical abacus. When 0s and 1s are written in a row to represent a number, each place in the row has a different value. The first 16 numbers in binary system are demonstrated.

Each time a 1 is added to an occupied place it is emptied and the 1 is placed in the first empty place on the left, and so on. Four additional numbers are given in the decimal system – can you translate them into binary?

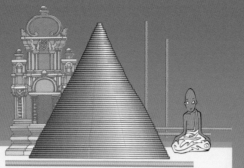

EDOUARD ANATOLE LUCAS (1842–91)

The French mathematician Edouard Anatole Lucas was best known for his work in number theory, including his studies of the Fibonacci sequence and the associated sequence called "Lucas" in his honour. One of his noted achievements was the proof that the Mersenne number $2^{127}-1$ is a prime number. This number remains the largest prime number discovered without the help of a computer. Lucas is also well known for his many mathematical recreations and puzzles, some of which appeared under the name of M. Claus (an anagram of Lucas). His four-volume work on recreational mathematics, *Recreations Mathematiques* (1882-94), has become a classic.

TOWER OF HANOI

"The End of the World Problem"

One of the most beautiful puzzles ever created, the Tower of Hanoi was invented by French mathematician Edouard Lucas (1842–91) in 1883. The puzzle contains three vertical posts in a line: at one end a number of rings of varying sizes are piled on one post, with the largest at the bottom. The game requires the player to move the discs from one end post to the other, never putting a larger ring on top of a smaller one and using the third post as a transfer site.

The puzzle is accompanied by a legend. At a great temple at Benares, India, there is a brass plate into which three vertical pins are fixed. At the beginning of time, 64 golden disks were stacked on one pin in decreasing order of size, with the largest resting at the bottom of the brass plate. Day and night, so the legend goes, a priest transfers the disks from one pin to another at a constant rate, never allowing any disk to be placed on top of a smaller one. Once the tower is rebuilt on one of the other two pins, the universe will end.

Even if the legend were true, there would be no reason to worry. Allowing one second per move of a disk, the task would take about 600 billion years, or about sixty times longer than the lifetime of the Sun. If the priest were devoting all his time and his whole life to the task, how many disks could he transfer?

The number of moves necessary to complete a Tower of Hanoi of a given smaller number of disks can be calculated as 2^n-1. So two disks require three moves, three disks require seven and so on.

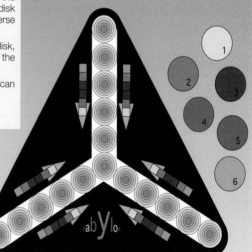

Initial configuration

The end configuration

BABYLON PUZZLE

The Babylon Puzzle is a design variation on the Tower of Hanoi. Initially the stack of six numbered disks are set up as shown. The object of the puzzle is to transfer the six disks to the right-hand channel in the same order, the highest number at bottom and decreasing numbers on top of it, keeping the following general rules:

(1) Move only one disk at a time.
(2) Do not place any disk on top of another disk of smaller value.
(3) The middle (vertical) channel may be used temporarily during the transfers, but observing rules (1) and (2).

How many moves will it take you to accomplish the transfer?

You can start playing this game on a lower level. First try to transfer only three disks (1,2, and 3), then four disks (1,2,3, and 4), then 5, before trying to tackle the problem of transferring the whole set of six disks.

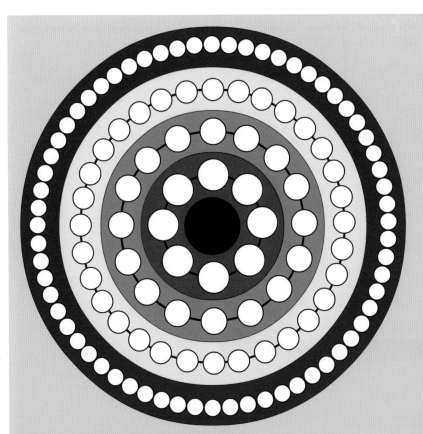

Four wheels

Red:	3-bit binary numbers
Green:	4-bit binary numbers
Yellow:	5-bit binary numbers
Blue:	6-bit binary numbers

 = 0

= 1

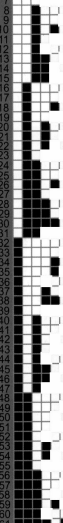

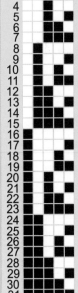

BINARY MEMORY WHEELS

The possible 3-bit, 4-bit, 5-bit, and 6-bit binary numbers can be described by three, four, five, or six switches, which may be in either the "on" or "off" position. These numbers represent the first 64 numbers (including 0) of the binary numbering system.

24 switches are necessary simultaneously to express the first eight 3-bit binary numbers; 64 switches for the 4-bit binary numbers; 160 switches for the 5-bit binary numbers; and 384 switches for the 6-bit binary numbers. However, in a binary wheel the same amount of information can be condensed to just 8, 16, 32, and 64 switches respectively – quite an economy! This can be accomplished by having the switches overlap.

Can you find a way to distribute the binary numbers along the binary wheels in such a way that all binary numbers will be represented by a set of adjacent "on" and "off" switches as you go around the wheels clockwise? Although the switches representing each number must be consecutive, the numbers themselves need not be distributed in a consecutive sequence.

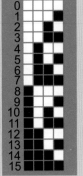

ZENO'S PARADOX OF ACHILLES AND THE TORTOISE RACE

The Ancient Greek mathematician Zeno of Elea, born in Italy around 490BCE, created more than 40 paradoxes to defend the teachings of the philosopher Parmenides, his teacher, who believed in monism: that reality is unchanging, and that change (motion) is impossible. Zeno's paradoxes seemed impossible to resolve at the time.

The most famous of Zeno's paradoxes is that of the race between Achilles and a tortoise. In the race, Achilles gives the tortoise a head start of 100 distance units, since he runs ten times as fast as the tortoise. Zeno's argument goes like this: Achilles runs 100 units and reaches the place where the tortoise started, but in that time the tortoise has run one-tenth as far as Achilles and so it is 10 units ahead of Achilles. Achilles runs this 10 units; meanwhile the tortoise runs one-tenth as far again and is now 1 unit in front of Achilles. Achilles runs this 1 unit; meanwhile the tortoise has run one-tenth of 1 unit and is therefore one-tenth of a unit in front of Achilles. So, argued Zeno, Achilles is always behind the tortoise, getting closer and closer, but can never catch him up. Zeno's conclusion was that it would take Achilles an infinite amount of time to catch

up with the tortoise and that his journey is divided into an infinite number of pieces.

In general, Zeno argued, before a moving object can travel a certain distance, it must travel half that distance. Before it can travel half the distance it must travel a quarter of the distance, and so on forever. The original distance cannot be traveled, and therefore motion is impossible. We know that motion is possible, so what is wrong with Zeno's logic? Can you find the faulty reasoning in Zeno's arguments?

His contemporaries played with geometry as people play with crossword puzzles and chess today. They recognized the fact that in reality Achilles would get past the tortoise; their problem was that their mathematics could not tell them where the catch was in Zeno's thinking. Greek geometry was timeless. They did not take time into account. Greek geometry could not make it obvious that Achilles would eventually overtake the tortoise. The new geometry developed by English scientist Sir Isaac Newton in the 17th and 18th centuries put time in the picture: our simple graph below clearly shows when and at what point Achilles will overtake the tortoise.

0
Start Achilles

100   110 111
Start tortoise

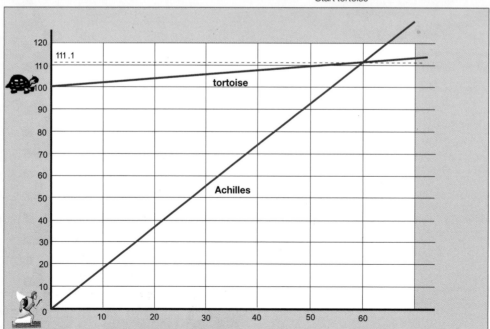

TRUTH, LIES AND IN BETWEEN

TRUTH CITY ROAD

The inhabitants of Truth City always speak the truth, while those of the city of Liars always lie. On your way to visit Truth City, you arrive at the crossroads leading to the two cities. As you can see, the sign is confusing, so you are forced to ask a man standing at the crossroads for the right direction. Unfortunately, you don't know whether the man is a liar or a truth-teller. You are allowed to ask the man only one question. What question can you ask him to be sure to learn how to get to Truth City?

TRUTH AND MARRIAGE

A king has two daughters, Amelia and Leila. One of them is married, and the other is not. Amelia always tells the truth, while Leila always lies. A young man is allowed to ask just one question of one of the daughters to find out which daughter is the married one. His reward would be marrying the unmarried daughter. The catch is, his question may not contain more than three words. Also, he does not know which daughter is which. What can he ask to win a bride?

060 6

TRUTH, LIES, AND IN BETWEEN

The inhabitants of the cosmopolitan city Nooneknowstruth are of three types: those who always speak the truth, those who always lie, and those who alternately lie and tell the truth. You meet one of the residents. You are allowed to ask him two questions. The answers must be sufficient for you to determine to which of the three groups the man belongs. What are the two questions you will ask him?

(The puzzles on this page were recorded at a fascinating lecture given by Raymond Smullyan at the Gathering for Gardner in Atlanta, Georgia, USA, in 2000)

VENN DIAGRAMS 1

Mathematical reasoning is based on a system of symbols and ideas that have precise meanings, a system of logic. We all possess an intuitive grasp of many principles of mathematical logic.

Mathematicians often apply logic to deduce conclusions from premises (starting points of a chain of logically connected ideas). "Venn diagrams" simplify relationships between two or more sets and can be a great help when performing deductions of this kind.

Devised by British logician and mathematician John Venn (1834-1923), Venn diagrams are patterns visualizing logical relationships between groups. A basic Venn diagram consists of a rectangle, the Universal set showing the space of all possible things. Within the rectangle, each set is represented by a circle. The overlapping regions imply that sharings are occurring.

Venn was keen to find symmetric diagrams, which he considered "elegant," and created a four-set Venn diagram using ellipses. D. W. Henderson and others showed that symmetric n Venn diagrams exist if and only if n is a prime number.

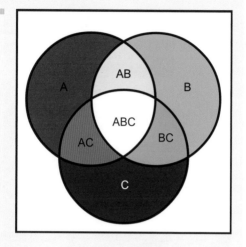

061 9

CAKES, JELLY, AND PUDDING

There are 99 children at a party. They are served jelly, pudding and cakes.

59 eat jelly; 22 eat pudding; 61 eat cake. 1 eats jelly, pudding and cake; 7 eat jelly and pudding; 4 eat pudding and cake. How many eat only one item? How many don't eat at all?

VENN DIAGRAMS

Branko Grunbaum, a mathematician at the University of Washington was the first person to show that there are symmetric Venn diagrams for five groups made from five congruent overlapping ellipses.

However, symmetrical Venn diagrams with seven petals were so hard to find that it was thought they do not exist. Nevertheless, others have gone further and in 2001 Dr. Peter Hamburger with Edith Hepp constructed the beautifully complex example for eleven petals, shown here.

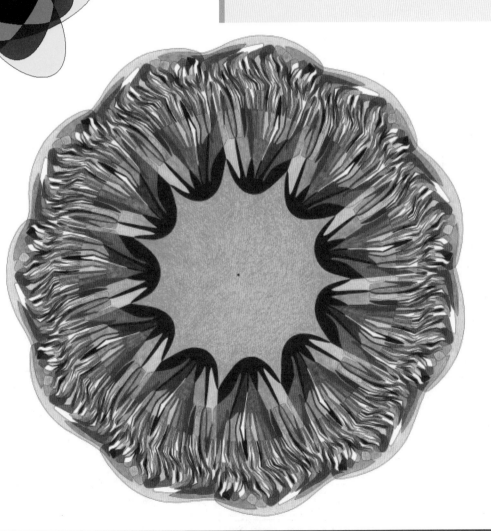

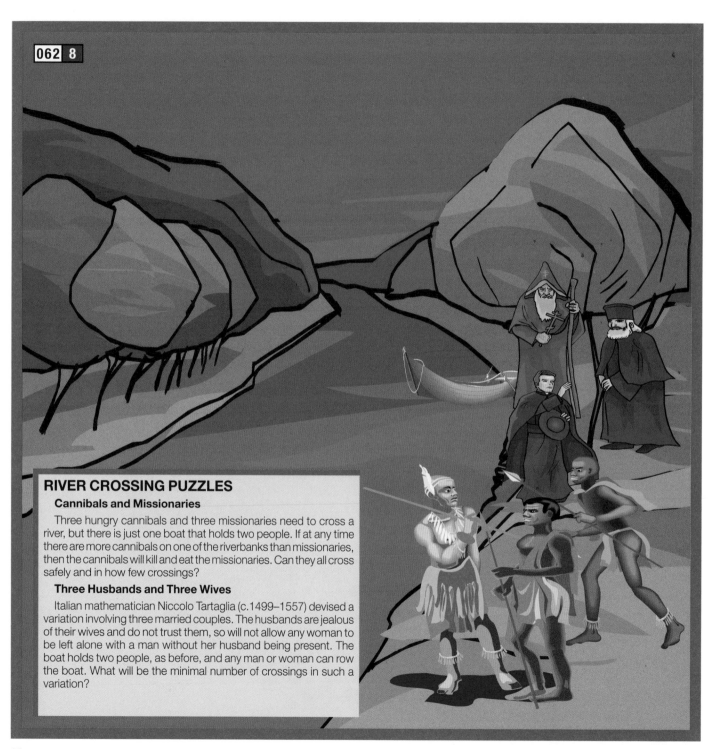

RIVER CROSSING PUZZLES

Cannibals and Missionaries

Three hungry cannibals and three missionaries need to cross a river, but there is just one boat that holds two people. If at any time there are more cannibals on one of the riverbanks than missionaries, then the cannibals will kill and eat the missionaries. Can they all cross safely and in how few crossings?

Three Husbands and Three Wives

Italian mathematician Niccolo Tartaglia (c.1499–1557) devised a variation involving three married couples. The husbands are jealous of their wives and do not trust them, so will not allow any woman to be left alone with a man without her husband being present. The boat holds two people, as before, and any man or woman can row the boat. What will be the minimal number of crossings in such a variation?

RIVER-CROSSING SOLDIERS

Three soldiers have to cross a river. Two boys pass by in a small boat and agree to help them, but their boat can support only one soldier or two boys. None of the soldiers can swim. Under these circumstances, how can they cross the river, end up on the other side and return the boat to the boys?

NIGHT CROSSING

Four hikers must cross a bridge in pitch darkness. The bridge will collapse in exactly 17 minutes. The hikers have only one flashlight, which is needed for each crossing. A maximum of two people can cross the bridge at one time carrying the flashlight, which must be returned after each crossing.

Each hiker walks at a different speed: it takes the first 1 minute to cross the bridge, the second 2 minutes, the third 5 minutes, and the fourth 10 minutes. Each pair crosses the bridge at the rate of the slower hiker – so, for example, hiker 1 with hiker 3 cross the bridge in 3 minutes.

How can all four hikers cross the bridge within 17 minutes? No tricks are permitted: the flashlight cannot be thrown back; no hiker is allowed to carry another. There are two possible solutions. Can you find both?

LAMP IN THE ATTIC

Puzzle 1 – The old castle has black curtains on the windows and a single lamp in the attic. At the entrance gate there are three light switches. One of them is for turning on the lamp in the attic. Your job is to find out which of the three switches activates the lamp, and you are allowed only one trip to the attic to check on the light. Can you figure out how to tell which light switch works?

Puzzle 2 - In the previous puzzle there were three switches but only one light – two switches had no use. This time there are three switches and three lamps in the castle, each lamp activated by one of the switches. As before, you are allowed to enter the castle only once to check the lights. How can you figure out now which lamp is switched on by which switch?

LANGFORD'S PROBLEMS

Puzzle 1 Four teams, two in each team

Examine the picture, which shows four teams of runners, with two runners in each team, pictured during a race. In the course of the race they change positions. At the finish line, their new configuration is as follows: one runner is between the red pair, two runners are between the blue pair, three runners are between the green pair, and four runners are between the yellow pair. All we can be sure of is that a yellow runner will be last. Can you tell what colors the first three runners are wearing?

Puzzle 2 Nine teams, three in each team

This time there are nine teams of runners, with three runners in each team. Each team wears a different color as shown and they are numbered in nine consecutive numbers: the three members of the first team all wear 1, the second team wears 2, and so on. At the finish line, the configuration of numbers is as follows: each numbered middle element in a triplet is separated from its outer triplets on both sides by their number. This is demonstrated, for example, for the number 2 triplet (see below), where a green no 2 finished third, sixth and ninth. Can you work out the configuration of the runners at the finish line?

separated by 2 runners on each side

84

HAT MAGIC

A magician puts four yellow, four green, and four red eggs in each hat. He calls a person from the audience, who (blindfolded) transfers five eggs from hat 1 to hat 2. The magician then asks the audience to tell the blindfolded assistant how many eggs have to be returned to hat 1 to ensure that, in hat 1, there will be at least three eggs of each of the three colors?

HATS AND COLORS 1

The series of logic puzzle classics based on mathematical induction, involving hats and colors, are gems of recreational mathematics, having endless variants. Two of these are shown.

The four clown are wearing 2 red and 2 green hats. None of them knows the color of his hat, and they are not allowed to turn and look back. Which of them will be the first to deduce the color of his hat and shout it aloud? Note:The first clown and his hat cannot be seen by the other clowns, since he is obstructed by the circus poster.

HATS AND COLORS 2

Three red hats and two blue hats have been shared out among five clowns. They are standing in a line (as shown) and clown E can be seen only by clown D. The colors of the hats of the clowns A and E (painted grey) are not known to us. None of the clowns knows the color of his hat, and they are not allowed to turn and look back. Which of them will be the first to deduce the color of clown A's hat and shout it aloud?

WATERMELON PARADOX

A restaurant diner is enjoying a big watermelon that originally weighed 10 kilograms and contained 90 per cent water. When it arrived at the restaurant its water content was reduced from the original 90 per cent to only 80 per cent.

Can you guess what was the total weight of the watermelon when it arrived at the table of the diner's table?

069 8

CONSECUTIVE WATERMELONS

Seven large watermelons had weights (in kilograms) of consecutive odd numbers, with their weights averaging 7 kilograms. What was the weight of the heaviest watermelon?

DRAGON FIGHT

A fearsome dragon has three heads and three tails. To kill the dragon, the hardy knight must cut off all the creature's heads and tails. But for all his bravery this is not an easy task.

With one swipe of his magic sword the knight can cut off one head, two heads, one tail, or two tails, but...

(1) When he cuts off one head, a new one grows in its place.
(2) When he cuts off one tail, two new tails replace it.
(3) When he cuts off two tails, one head grows instead.
(4) When he chops off two heads, nothing grows.

How many swipes of the magic sword will the knight need to kill the dragon?

BIRTHDAY PROBLEMS

(1) How large does a randomly selected group have to be for there to be a better than even chance of two members of the group sharing the same birthday?

(2) How many people, in addition to yourself, should there be in a group in order for the probability that at least one of them has the same birthday as you to be more than 50 per cent?

If you want to get lucky ... it pays to be ready... (and to know a bit of probability).

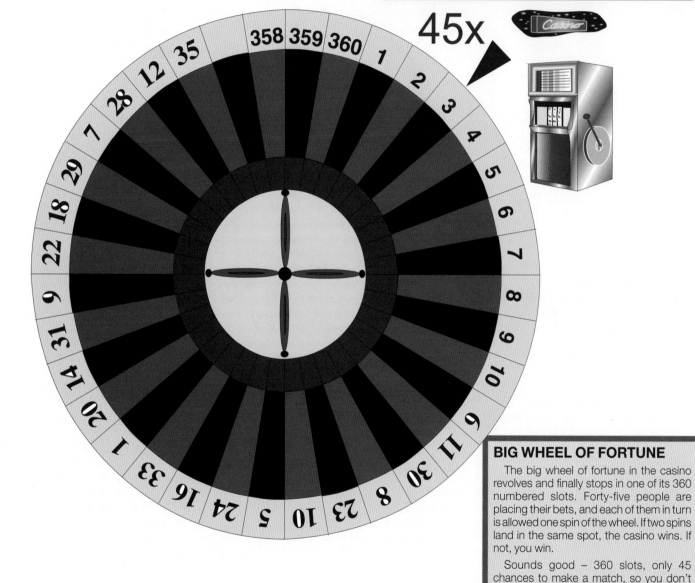

45x

BIG WHEEL OF FORTUNE

The big wheel of fortune in the casino revolves and finally stops in one of its 360 numbered slots. Forty-five people are placing their bets, and each of them in turn is allowed one spin of the wheel. If two spins land in the same spot, the casino wins. If not, you win.

Sounds good – 360 slots, only 45 chances to make a match, so you don't hesitate to bet. You are sure your chances of winning are high. Aren't they?

COIN TOSSING

COIN TOSSING AND CHANCE

During the early 1700s, French mathematician Abraham De Moivre (1667–1754) laid the foundation for probability theory in his important book The Doctrine of Chances. He explained probability through problems dealing with dice, coins, and games.

One of the many interesting thing about De Moivre is that he did not really believe in chance. He hypothesized that nothing ever happened "by chance" – every seemingly random event could actually be traced back to a physical cause.

His position can be explained as follows. If you were to measure all the physical factors that go into a coin flip – the angle of your hand, its distance from the ground, the force you use to toss the coin into the air, the wind currents, the composition of the coin, and so on, and so on – then you'd be able to predict a flip's outcome with 100 per cent accuracy, because the coin is subject to the laws of Newtonian physics, which are absolute. We can't do all this, and therefore events may appear random even though they are entirely determined by physical phenomena. This school of thought is today called determinism.

THREE COINS FLIP

What are the chances of three coins turning up alike – that is, either all heads or all tails?

Will the following reasoning provide the right answer?

When throwing three coins, at least two of the coins must come up alike. Since there is an even chance for a third coin to turn up heads or tail, the chance of all three coins turning up alike should be 1 to 1... or should it?

FLIPPING A COIN FIVE TIMES

If you toss a coin five times in a row, how many different outcomes are possible?

FLIPPING COIN GAME

Two players are playing a simple game by tossing a single coin in turn. The winner is the first player to throw a head. Which player has a higher chance to win? Do both players have an equal chance of winning the game?

BALANCING COINS

Balance 20 or more pennies on their edges on a perfectly smooth horizontal table – you may need a little patience! Now slam your hand on the table, making all the coins topple over. Count the heads and tails. You will be quite surprised. Your repeat experiments will tend to confirm the outcome of significantly more tails than heads showing up. Can you explain why?

COIN-TOSSING AND PROBABILITY

When a coin is tossed into the air no one can say which way it will land. Yet toss that coin a million times and it will, with increasingly minor variations, come up heads half the time and tails the rest. In essence, this is the basis of the theory of probability.

Essentially two laws underlie probability, a both-and law (to calculate the probability of two events both happening) and an either-or law (to calculate the probability of one or the other of two events happening).

The both-and law states that the chance of two independent events both happening is equal to the probability of one happening multiplied by the probability of the other happening. For instance, the chance of one flip of a coin coming up heads is 1/2. The chance of heads landing face up on both a first and a second flip is 1/2 x 1/2, or only 1/4.

The either-or law states that the chance of one or the other of two mutually exclusive probabilities coming true equals the sum of the separate chance of each coming true individually. For instance, the chance of turning up either heads or tails on a flip of a coin is equal to the chance of throwing heads plus the chance of throwing tails: 1/2 + 1/2 = 1.

There are four possible results when tossing two coins (or making two tosses of a single coin).
(1) Heads first, Heads second;
(2) Tails first, Tails second;
(3) Heads first, Tails second;
(4) Tails first, Heads second.

The probability of a toss of heads and tails occurring (2:4 = 1:2) is twice as high as that of either of the other two combinations (both 1:4).

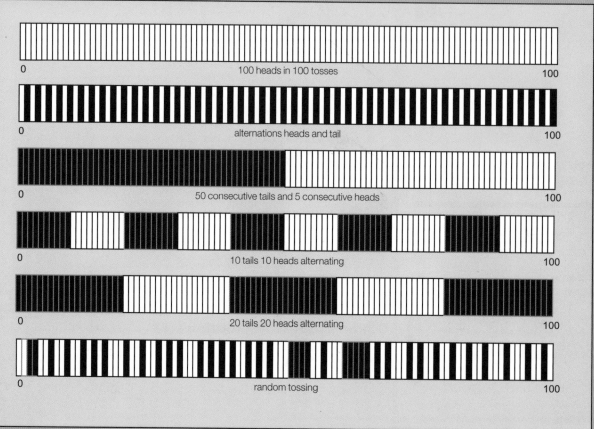

0   100 heads in 100 tosses   100

0   alternations heads and tail   100

0   50 consecutive tails and 5 consecutive heads   100

0   10 tails 10 heads alternating   100

0   20 tails 20 heads alternating   100

0   random tossing   100

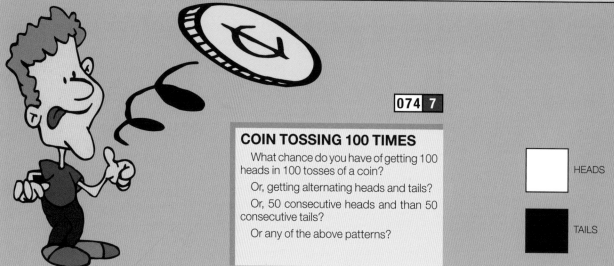

074 7

COIN TOSSING 100 TIMES

What chance do you have of getting 100 heads in 100 tosses of a coin?

Or, getting alternating heads and tails?

Or, 50 consecutive heads and than 50 consecutive tails?

Or any of the above patterns?

HEADS

TAILS

92

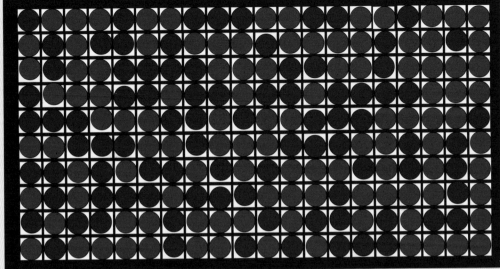

Test 2

 Heads

 Tails

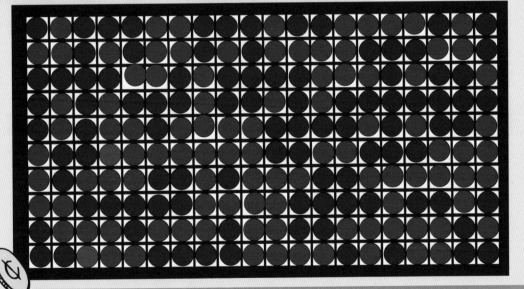

BENFORD'S LAW

Discovering Fakes or The Tossing a Coin 200 Times Experiment

Dr. Theodore P. Hill asked his mathematics students at the Georgia Institute of Technology to go home and do one of two things: either flip a coin 250 times and record the experiment; or, just pretend to flip a coin and fake the 250 tosses. When he checked their result, to the enormous amazement of his students, he easily identified all those who faked the results.

Here are two records of tossing 250 coins, one of them a fake. Can you find it?

SCATTERHEAD
The power of statistical sampling

The Scatterhead is a toy which can demonstrate the statistical method of taking a small sample to deduce the properties of a much larger set.

The Scatterhead contains 60 small balls in four different colors: green, yellow, blue, and red. We don't know how many balls of each color there are. When we give Scatterhead a spin its head will revolve, mixing the balls inside. When the head is back in its normal position, different random combinations of ten colored balls appear in the eyes, nose, and mouth.

Below are six different random outcomes of spinning the Scatterhead. Can you estimate the number of balls of each color hidden in the head?

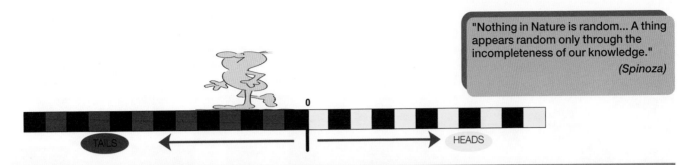

RANDOM WALK

For this puzzle flip a coin repeatedly: If it comes down heads the walker will move one mark to the right; if tails he will move one mark to the left. After many flips of the coin, let's say 36 flips, can you guess how far from his starting point our walker will be?

After your guess, flip the coin 36 times to check your prediction. Can you also tell, what the chances are that our walker will return to his starting point at some point in his walk? (Assume that the walk continues indefinitely.)

077 **9**

RANDOM DRUNKARD'S WALK

In the drunkard's randomwalk, starting from the central lamppost, moves are dictated by flipping two coins (a red and yellow coin), as shown. This is the simplest demonstration of a stochastic process, and a good analogy for explaining Brownian motion, in which a particle is "kicked around" by molecules of a surrounding liquid or gas.

Where do you think the drunkard will be after a certain number of flips (N)? Can you also guess what the chances will be that the drunkard will return to his starting point at the lamppost at some point? Consider the walk as finite by considering the size of the grid as a barrier. What happens when he reaches the edge, then?

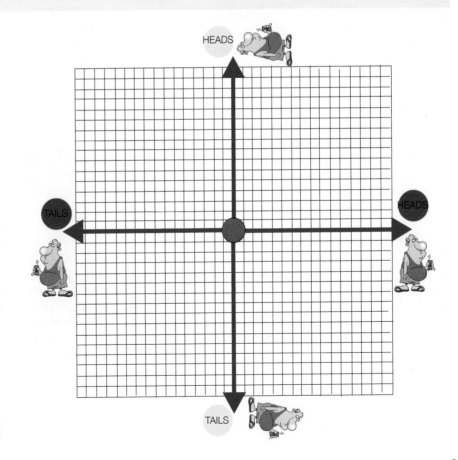

95

RANDOM PATTERNS?

Which of the two patterns appears to offer the most random placement of its fifty white and fifty black cells?

1	2	3	4	5	6	7	8	9	10	ordered
6	3	8	1	7	5	9	2	8	4	biased toward 8
6	2	5	8	4	7	1	10	3	9	unbiased
4	8	3	5	10	2	7	?	1	9	unbiased the empty space must be 6

RANDOM DIGITS PARADOX

Try to arrange the first 10 digits from the ordered sequence into a random one?

If you duplicate one or more digits, the series shows a bias toward those digits. If it is completely free from bias, it will contain each of the 10 digits. But in this case, the sequence will be strongly "patterned", and if you select any nine digits, the missing digit can be guessed with certainty. Similar contradictions turn up in connection with any random series. If it gets too random, a "pattern of disorder" appears.

So we are faced with a curious paradox.

Mathematicians agree that an absolutely disordered series of digits is a logically contradictory concept. We have demonstrated that as a series of digits comes closer to an absolutely patternless series, we get a pattern we may suspect has been carefully constructed by a mathematician rather than generated by random chance.

A number series can be no more patternless than an arrangement of stars in the sky. And throughout history, star-gazers have seen an endless number of patterns in the sky.

078 8

TRIPLE DUEL

Tom, Bill, and Mike decide to settle their differences by first drawing straws to determine the order in which they will shoot and then each taking one shot at the target of their choice until only one is standing. Tom and Bill are perfect shots and never miss, while Mike is only average and has a 50% success rate. Who has the best chance of survival?

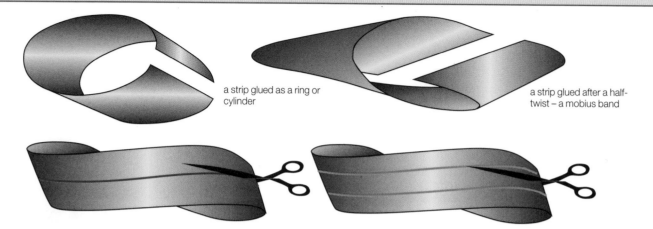

a strip glued as a ring or cylinder

a strip glued after a half-twist – a mobius band

MOEBIUS BAND CUT ALONG THE MIDDLE

Cut a Mobius band along the center all around the red line until you come back to where you started. What will be the outcome?

MOEBIUS BAND CUT NEAR THE EDGE

Cut a Mobius band along the green line which is near the edge. What will be the outcome?

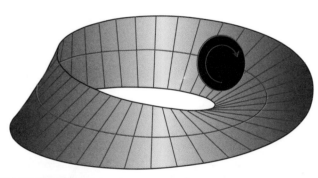

TRAVELLER'S PATH ALONG A MOEBIUS BAND

What will happen to a traveler and his watch when he travels along a Moebius band and comes back to the point where he started? Try to work it out on the example you've made!

MOEBIUS BAND
A Beautiful Object with a Mysterious Twist

The nineteenth-century German mathematician A.F. Moebius (1790-1868) discovered that it was possible to make a surface that has only one side and one edge and has no "inside" and "outside", unlike a cylinder, torus or a sphere. Of course the paper has a certain thickness which is ignored.

Although such an object seems impossible to imagine, making a Moebius strip is very simple: take a strip of ordinary paper and give one end a twist, then glue the two ends together. You've created a Moebius strip, just like that.

A Moebius strip is the basis of an endless number of exciting structures, puzzles and with many surprising and paradoxical properties that have led to important developments in topology.

Can you have the insight to figure out what will be the outcome of cutting a Moebius band along the middle? Or cutting it along a line near its edge? And what will happen to a traveler and his watch when he travels along a Moebius band and comes back to his starting point?

Can you find a real-life object, which you can even touch, and which is truly two-dimensional?

NON-TRANSITIVITY

Most relationships are *transitive*, which is the word for a binary relationship that states: if A is bigger than B, and B is bigger than C, then A must also be bigger than C. However, some relationships are not transitive. For example, if A is the father of B, and B is the father of C, it is never true that A is the father of C.

The well-known children's game called "stone-scissors-paper" children's game is non-transitive. In this game the relationships of stone breaking scissors, scissors cutting paper, and paper wrapping ston create the winning rules.

Ancient Chinese philosophers divided matter into five categories forming a non-transitive cycle: wood gives birth to fire; fire gives birth to earth; earth gives birth to metal; metal gives birth to water; and water gives birth to wood.

In probability theory there are relationships that appear to be transitive when actually they are not. If this nontransitivity is so counter-intuitive as to boggle the mind, these relationships are called "nontransitive paradoxes or games".

A great deal of ingenuity went into creating such paradoxes and games, which are also perfect "sucker bets", because it's so hard to believe the proposition, most people will "intuitively" bet against it … and lose.

One of the simplest and most astonishing of such games is the non-transitive dice sets, like the set in our puzzle. Such dice were first designed by Bradley Efron, at Stanford University, and then they were opened to wider audiences by Martin Gardner in his regular column in Scientific American magazine.

NON-TRANSITIVE DICE

If you are playing a game using dice, you expect the numbers that you throw to be random. The object of this game is to find out what is special about the four dice in being used here.

The first thing to do is to make a set of four dice as shown. After you've done that:

1. Ask a partner to choose one of the four dice, while you choose one of the remaining three.

2. Taking turns, throw each dice, and as usual the higher number wins.

3. The trick is to decide if you can always choose the dice that will make you win in the long run?

081 6

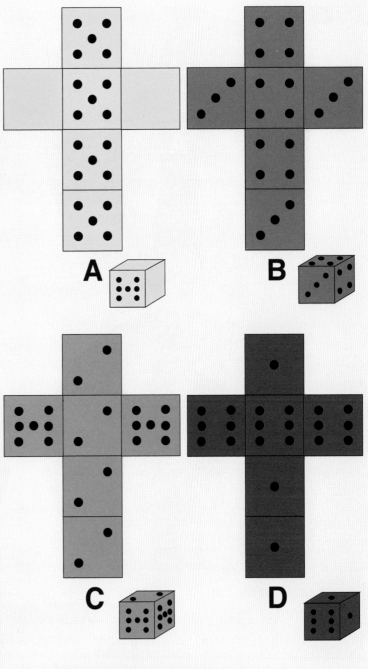

NON-TRANSITIVE DICE

The nets of the four nontransitive dice

NON-TRANSITIVE SPINNERS

Two players each choose one of the spinners and play a series of rounds; the higher number wins each round. Can you work out the winning odds between any two spinners so that you can have the advantage no matter what spinner your opponent chooses?

FIFTH COLOR

On 1 April 1975 Martin Gardner published the map shown here, which was designed by William McGregor so it could not be colored by fewer than five colors, as shown below. The map is shown below requiring a fifth color. Can you do better?

the fifth color

FOUR-COLOR THEOREM

How many colors do you need to color any map in such a way that no adjacent regions have the same color? The adjacent regions must touch along an edge, not just at a point.

This is what was until recently called the "Four-color problem," first stated by South African mathematician Francis Guthrie (1831–99) in 1852.

It is not hard to show that at least four colors are needed. In 1879 British mathematician Alfred Kempe (1849-1922) published a proof that no map needed five colors. Ten years later it was noticed that he had made a subtle but crucial mistake, and that his proof actually showed that no map required six colors.

This left a tantalizing gap, and for around 100 years mathematicians wrestled with the problem. No-one could find a map that actually needed five colors, but equally no-one could show conclusively that no such map existed. This became notorious as one of the simplest remaining classical unsolved mathematical problems.

To make matters worse, analogous problems dealing with more complicated surfaces could be answered conclusively. For example, a map on a doughnut can always be colored with seven colors, and there exist maps for which six colors do the job; on a strange one-sided surface called a Klein bottle, six colors are both necessary and sufficient.

Then in 1976 Kenneth Appel and Wolfgang Haken at the University of Illinois solved the problem using a supercomputer, and so now we have the Four-Color theorem: for any map in the plane four colors are sufficient to color it in such a way that no adjacent regions have the same color.

Many recreational mathematics problems are based on the problem of how many colors will be needed to color a given map or pattern so that neighboring regions are all differently colored. Often such problems can also be played as competition games between players. The difficulty of seeing in advance the potential color "cul-de-sacs" that can occur when coloring maps, seemingly making it necessary to have a fifth color, makes these problems and games challenging.

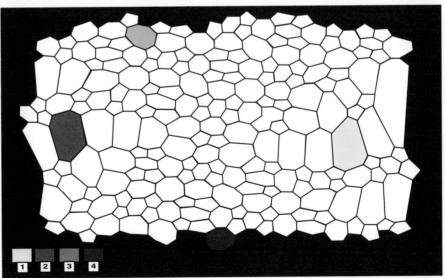

1 2 3 4

KNIGHT'S TOURS

In chess the knight moves either two squares horizontally and one vertically or two vertically and one horizontally.

One of the oldest and most interesting chessboard puzzles is "The Knight's Tour," created in 1700 by English mathematician Brook Taylor (1685–1731). Is there a series of legal moves that will make the knight visit every square of the board once and once only? The size of the board need not be the usual chessboard of eight squares by eight squares.

Mathematically, this is a question about graphs. Think of the squares on the board as nodes, and join the nodes by an edge if there is a legal knight's move that connects them.

The tour is "closed" is the knight returns to his original home on the final move. Closed tours can occur on even-sided boards. To see this, note that the knight changes the color of his square on each move if the squares are in the normal checkered pattern. On an odd-sided board, the knight makes an even number of moves to visit every square, so if he takes one more move to return to the square he started from that move would have to be to a square coloured differently to his starting square, which is clearly impossible.

On the standard chessboard, there are at least several million different knight's tours. Swiss mathematician Leonard Euler (1707-83) found many unusual symmetries. Here we show some original designs based on closed knight's tours. Discovering and colouring knight's tours is a challenging activity.

You can create knight's tours by numbering the squares of a board to indicate the knight's progress. An alternative way of representing the same path is to draw a continuous line from the center of the squares. The visual patterns created in this way are often aesthetically pleasing. Copying the basic grid, you can color and preserve the tours. It is also an interesting challenge to devise knight's tours on a rectangular board or those of other shapes.

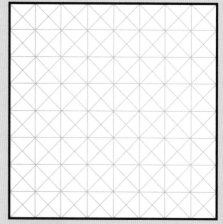

Create your own knight's tours

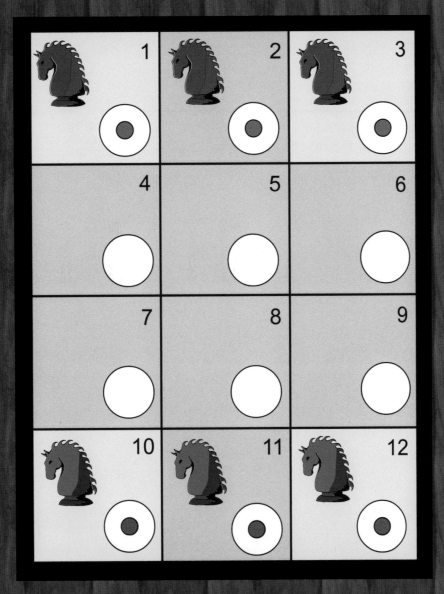

KNIGHTS EXCHANGE

The knights move as in Chess. What is the smallest number of moves to exchange the places of the two sets of three knights?

Play Pieces

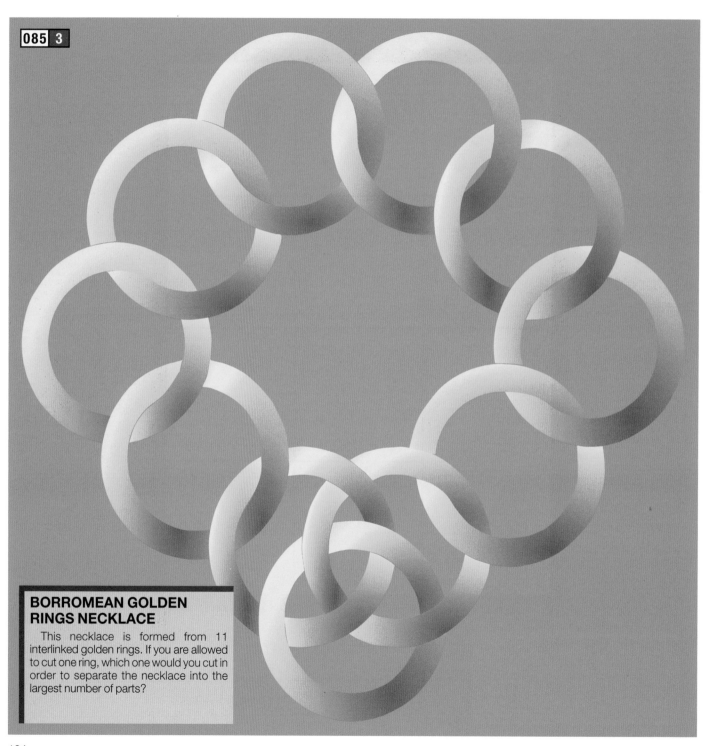

BORROMEAN GOLDEN RINGS NECKLACE

This necklace is formed from 11 interlinked golden rings. If you are allowed to cut one ring, which one would you cut in order to separate the necklace into the largest number of parts?

ALHAMBRA

`086` `6`

THE ALHAMBRA

Built between 1238 and 1358 on a hill overlooking Granada in Spain, the Alhambra was the palace and fortress of the Islamic Moorish kings of Spain. After the expulsion of the Moors from Spain in 1492, the structures were greatly damaged, but were later expensively restored. The Alhambra is one of the finest examples of the once-flourishing Moorish civilization in Spain. The interiors of the buildings are decorated with magnificent examples of geometric ornamentation of minute detail and intricacy.

ALHAMBRA MOSAIC PATTERN

The former palace of the Moorish kings of Granada is a treasure house of mathematical beauty. The intricate pattern shown is one of its many complex geometrical designs. Can you tell whether the design is one loop or whether it is composed of separate parts? If so, how many?

ABSTRACT ART

The prohibition of figurative art, on religious grounds, was taken seriously by both Arabs and Hebrews, who developed a purely abstract and geometric art tradition instead. One of the best examples of the supreme quality of this tradition is reflected in the 14th century tilings of the Alhambra in Granada, Spain.

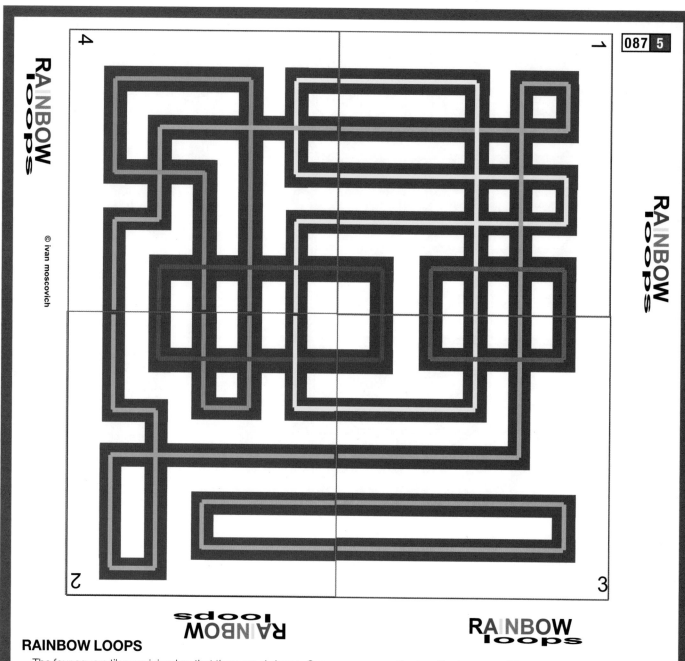

RAINBOW LOOPS

The four square tiles are joined so that there are six loops. Can you rearrange the four tiles to create different patterns? How many can you create? Can you rearrange the four tiles in the same square configuration to form one to six loops?

Copy the image and cut out the four squares along the fine lines that divide them.

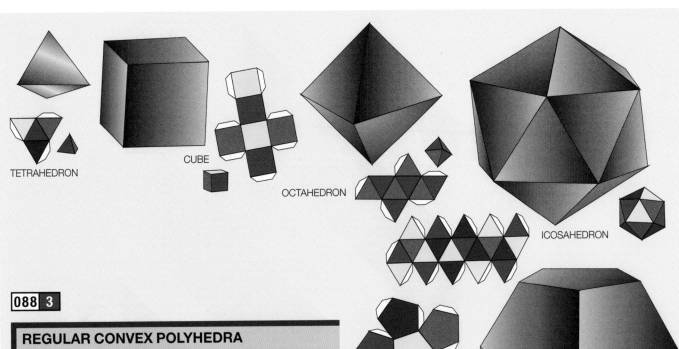

TETRAHEDRON

CUBE

OCTAHEDRON

ICOSAHEDRON

REGULAR CONVEX POLYHEDRA

A polyhedron (plural polyhedra) is a three-dimensional geometric object with a number of flat faces joined at straight edges. Its name comes from the Ancient Greek words poly ("many") and edron ("face"). The regular convex polyhedra have equivalent faces composed of convex regular polygons. There are only five regular polyhedra – the Tetrahedron (four faces), the Cube (six faces), the Octahedron (eight faces), the Dodecahedron (12 faces), and the Icosahedron (20 faces). It is astonishing that there are only five, given the fact that there are an unlimited number of regular polygons.

Polyhedra are the ultimate blending of mathematics and art. Their abstract purity and perfection delights all lovers of form and symmetry. They have fascinated humankind for centuries. The ancient Greeks knew and proved that there are only five regular polyhedra. They considered them the most beautiful objects in the world. The regular convex polyhedra are also called the Platonic solids after the Ancient Greek philosopher Plato (428–348BCE). He argued that the elements of fire, earth, air and water were made from the regular polyhedra.

Three-dimensional models of solids created from their nets are often used as an introduction to basic concepts of space geometry. You can make volume and area comparisons with models of solids, and use them in different combinations to create a variety of aesthetic structures, puzzles, and games. As a DIY art-craft activity, creating the demonstrated mobile of the five Platonic solids is an enjoyable and rewarding pastime.

DODECAHEDRON

REGULAR POLYHEDRA CHART

Can you fill in the characteristics of the five regular solids?

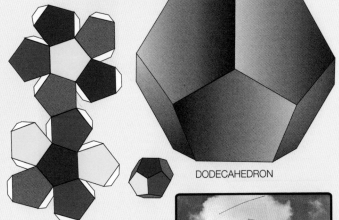

Solid	Vertices (V)	Edges (E)	Faces (F)	V - E + F
Tetrahedron				
Cube				
Octahedron				
Icosahedron				
Dodecahedron				

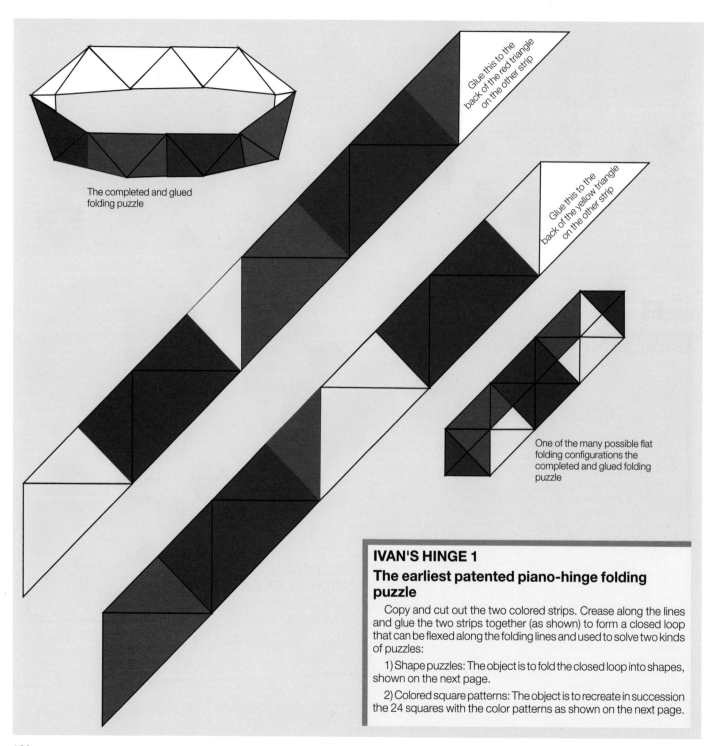

The completed and glued folding puzzle

Glue this to the back of the red triangle on the other strip

Glue this to the back of the yellow triangle on the other strip

One of the many possible flat folding configurations the completed and glued folding puzzle

IVAN'S HINGE 1

The earliest patented piano-hinge folding puzzle

Copy and cut out the two colored strips. Crease along the lines and glue the two strips together (as shown) to form a closed loop that can be flexed along the folding lines and used to solve two kinds of puzzles:

1) Shape puzzles: The object is to fold the closed loop into shapes, shown on the next page.

2) Colored square patterns: The object is to recreate in succession the 24 squares with the color patterns as shown on the next page.

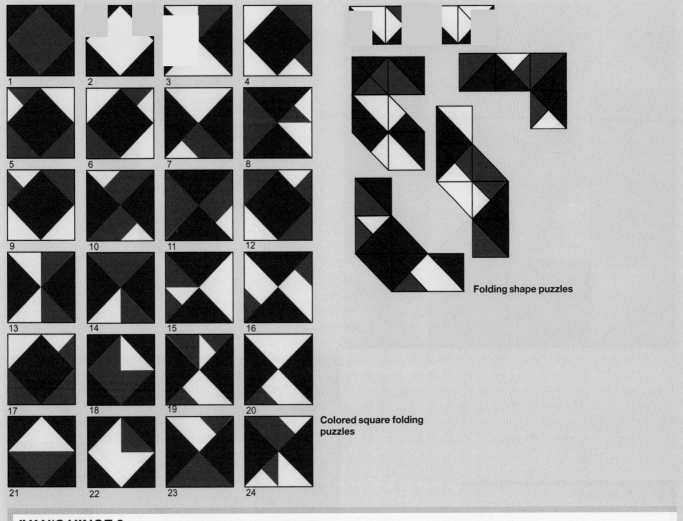

Folding shape puzzles

Colored square folding puzzles

IVAN'S HINGE 2
24 colored square puzzles and a sample selection of shape puzzles.

From *The Piano-Hinged Dissections: Time to Fold!* by Greg N. Frederickson, the ultimate book on the history of folding puzzles:

"Later on, another surprise awaited me. I learned of a loop of sixteen isosceles right triangles that forms a square and all the other tetrominos (figures from four squares). Entitled 'Ivan's Hinge,' it was marketed by the puzzle company Paradigm Games, also in the mid-to-late-1990s.

"The Israeli puzzle designer and author Ivan Moscovich, together with Jan Essebaggers, patented the loop of sixteen isosceles right triangles (1994). It is not clear whether Moscovich realized that his loop would form all of the tetrominos, in the same fashion as Stevens's creation. He seemed primarily interested in forming the square, and the patent application also pointed out that a loop of 64 triangles would form a 4x4 square. However, Moscovich marketed it not only as a puzzle but also as a promotional item for a variety of entities, such as the Eastman Kodak Company and the Mid Glamorgan Economic Development Unit in Cardiff, Wales, and many other."

Front

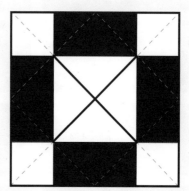

FLEXI-TWIST

Flexi-twist is an original folding puzzle I created in the 1970s. It is like 12 puzzles in one.

Copy and cut out the square with the patterns printed on both sides as shown. Crease and fold both ways along the fold lines. Cut through the two diagonals in the middle yellow square.

In succession, fold along the fold lines only to create a square half size with the patterns shown on the opposite page.

Back

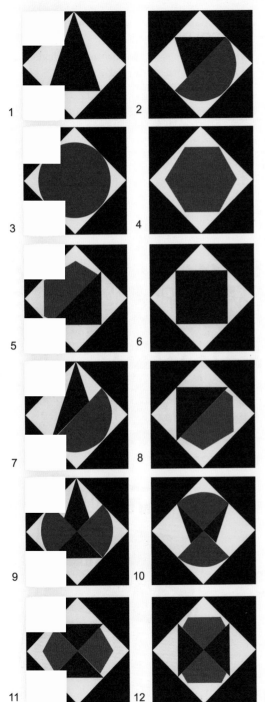

1
2
3
4
5
6
7
8
9
10
11
12

FLEXI-TWIST 2

Many mathematical, geometrical, and topological discoveries can be made simply by folding a square piece of paper. These activities can provide an excellent introduction to plane geometry for both children and adults. The ancient art of Origami and the 20th-century development of the flexagon are good examples.

A flexagon is a paper structure that can be folded to produce a series of flat faces. Flexagon maker Adam Walsh defined them as flat pieces of paper that have more faces to them then the "obvious" two. The first flexagon was created in 1939 by Princeton student Arthur Stone as he played around with a strip of paper. Thereafter the use of folding paper in mathematical recreations became very popular.

I became fascinated by flexagons in the early 1950s, when Martin Gardner introduced them to wide audiences. I subsequently created several original folding structures that loosely belong in the category of flexagons.

One of the structures I developed was the Flexi-twist. I had set myself the challenge of creating interesting folding puzzles that did not require pre-folding and gluing (as classical Flexagons did), but still had an impressive number of "faces" and puzzle objectives. The Flexi-twist was the result.

Another of my structures was the Magistrip, which was produced in the UK under the name of "Ivan's Hinge," and "Magic Mat."

Robert E. Neale, the world's top expert and creator of folding puzzles, created a great variety of remarkable paper folding structures and novel flexagons.

FLEXI-TWIST FOLDING PUZZLES

FOLDING PUZZLES

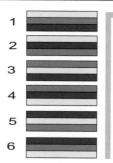

FOLDING THREE STAMPS

Just by looking, can you tell how many different ways you can fold a strip of three stamps? You may only fold on the perforations and the end result must be of three stamps on top of each other. It does not matter whether the stamps are face-up or face-down.

There are six possible permutations of three colors as shown.

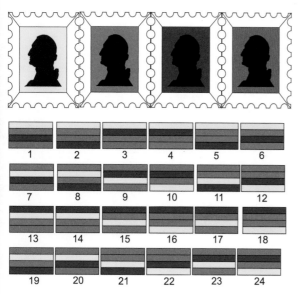

FOLDING FOUR STAMPS

Just by looking, can you tell how many different ways you can fold a strip of four stamps? As before, you may only fold on the perforations, and the end result must be a stack of four stamps on top of each other. It does not matter whether the stamps are face-up or face-down. There are 24 possible permutations of four colors as shown. How many can you achieve?

MAP FOLDING

In how many different ways can a map be folded?

Polish mathematician Stanislaw Ulam (1909–84) was the first pose the question. The problem has frustrated researchers in the field of modern combinatorial theory ever since. Indeed, the general problem of map folding is still unsolved.

089 3

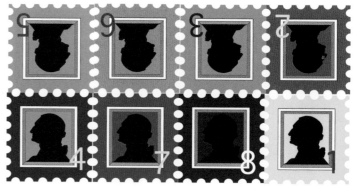

FOLDING EIGHT STAMPS

Can you fold the block of eight stamps along their perforations so that the stamps are stacked in order from 1 to 8?

FOLDING NEWS

How many times do you think you will be able to fold a page of a newspaper in half? Five times? Eight times? More than ten times? Try it and find out!

FOLDING PUZZLES 2

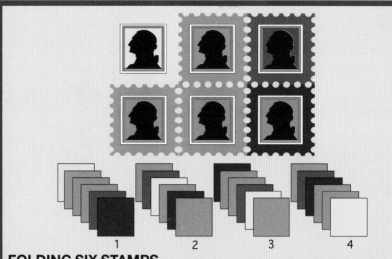

1   2   3   4

FOLDING SIX STAMPS

Six stamps are joined in a two-by-three rectangle. It can be folded in many ways along the stamps' perforated sides to create a stack of stamps.

Four stacks are shown in color sequences. Can you tell which stack is impossible to fold? You can imagine the stamps colored the same on both sides, so it does not matter which side of a stamp is "up" in the final folded stack.

FOLDING A SQUARE OF STAMPS

Just by looking, can you tell how many different ways you can fold a square of four stamps? You may only fold on the perforations and the end result must be a stack of four stamps on top of each other. It does not matter whether the stamps are face-up or face-down.

There are 24 permutations of four colors, as previously shown. How many can you achieve by folding?

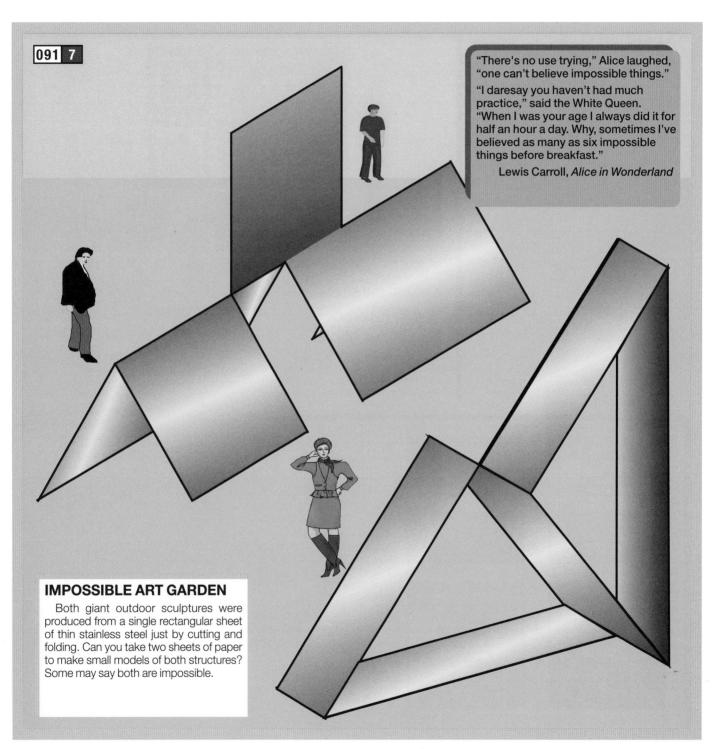

"There's no use trying," Alice laughed, "one can't believe impossible things."

"I daresay you haven't had much practice," said the White Queen. "When I was your age I always did it for half an hour a day. Why, sometimes I've believed as many as six impossible things before breakfast."

Lewis Carroll, *Alice in Wonderland*

IMPOSSIBLE ART GARDEN

Both giant outdoor sculptures were produced from a single rectangular sheet of thin stainless steel just by cutting and folding. Can you take two sheets of paper to make small models of both structures? Some may say both are impossible.

THE IMPOSSIBLE TRIANGLE

What is the greatest illusion of all, if not the *illusion of impossibility*?

Professor Roger Penrose invented the impossible triangle and first drew it on paper. It looked like this:

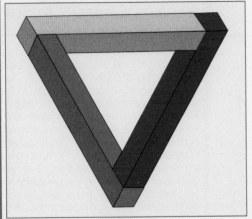

At first glance you think you are looking at a familiar object, but soon you realize something is wrong about it. The corners of the impossible triangle make sense: but the overall view is confusing and impossible to create. If you tried to build it, you would not be able to finish.

For many years interested parties accepted that it would be impossible to build Penrose's famous impossible triangle. But then Professor Richard Gregory built it. In the photograph (above right) you can see a version of the triangle as later reproduced by John Beetlestone (the director of the hands-on museum Techniquest in Cardiff). Bettlestone built the triangle in a giant size, large enough for visitors to walk through at the entrance to the museum.

But did Professor Gregory really build an impossible triangle? No. What he did was build a simple structure which, when viewed from a particular location, looks exactly like the Penrose impossible triangle. When you look at the structure from this particular point, the two ends of the arms line up and the perceptual system of the brain assumes that they lie in one plane. And because of this false assumption, you "see" a completed triangle.

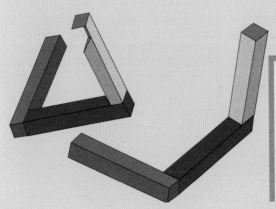

GATES – IMPOSSIBLE OR POSSIBLE?

The three gates (above right) provide a good demonstration of the difference between simple flat planes and multiple planes on which many impossible figures are based. A multiple plane looks like a flat plane when viewed from one point in the drawing, but consists of two or more planes when seen from another point in the same drawing. Looking at the plan of the base (right), it is easy to see which gates are impossible objects.

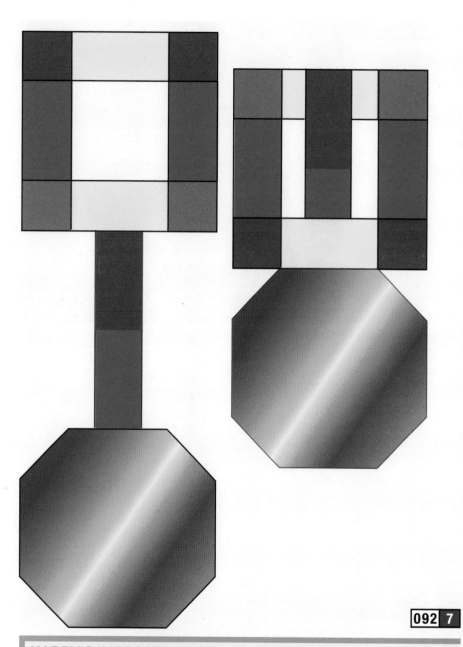

HARRY'S IMPOSSIBLE LOOP FOLDING PUZZLE

The object of the puzzle is to fold the sheet only along the black folding lines to make the big octagon pass through the loop as shown. (The puzzle was invented by Harry Eng. I received it as a souvenir of the International Puzzle Party on 11 June 1994.)

> "The impossible takes just a bit longer"
> *Harry Eng*

HARRY'S IMPOSSIBLE LOOP THE IMPOSSIBLE

If you had said to a major scientist in 1900 that in 2000, just a hundred years later, satellites would transmit pictures to your home, millions of people would take to the air every day and you could cross the Atlantic at 2,000 miles per hour, that humans would have visited the Moon, that people would carry telephones weighing a few ounces and speak anywhere in the world without wires, or that most of these miracles would depend on devices the size of a postage stamp – if you had said all this, the scientist would almost certainly have pronounced you quite mad. Most of these developments could not have been predicted in 1900 because prevailing science said they were impossible.

Accurately predicting the future is not an easy thing to do, as anyone who tries it quickly learns. History is filled with bold forecasts by experts that did not quite pan out.

In everyday language when we say something is impossible, we often do not mean that it is impossible in any circumstances; we simply mean that we cannot see any way to achieve it. In mathematics, however, impossibility is something we often can prove.

Imagine you convince yourself that you have discovered a new prime number, thousands of digits long. Its final digit is 6. In high excitement you dispatch it to a leading mathematician, who sends it immediately back with a note that it is nonsense. You ask him where you made the mistake, and he answers that he hasn't read your work and he has no idea where the mistake came. In everyday life you would be frustrated. But in mathematics his response is simply logical. It has been proven that the only even prime number is 2. There are no others.

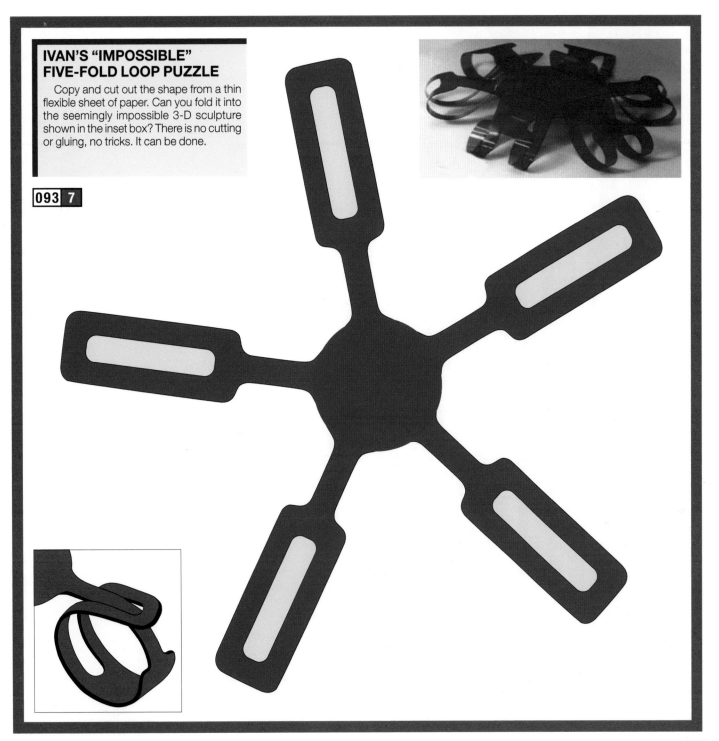

IVAN'S "IMPOSSIBLE" FIVE-FOLD LOOP PUZZLE

Copy and cut out the shape from a thin flexible sheet of paper. Can you fold it into the seemingly impossible 3-D sculpture shown in the inset box? There is no cutting or gluing, no tricks. It can be done.

093 7

117

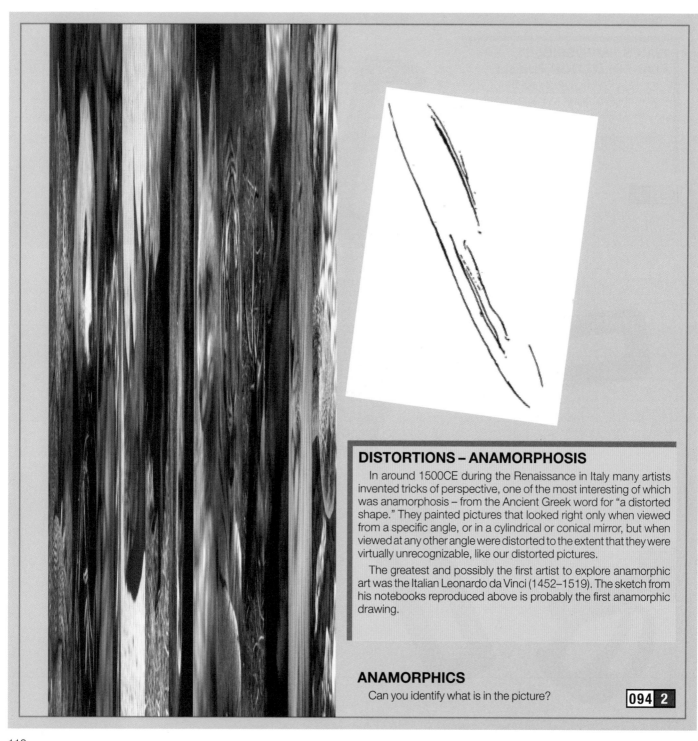

DISTORTIONS – ANAMORPHOSIS

In around 1500CE during the Renaissance in Italy many artists invented tricks of perspective, one of the most interesting of which was anamorphosis – from the Ancient Greek word for "a distorted shape." They painted pictures that looked right only when viewed from a specific angle, or in a cylindrical or conical mirror, but when viewed at any other angle were distorted to the extent that they were virtually unrecognizable, like our distorted pictures.

The greatest and possibly the first artist to explore anamorphic art was the Italian Leonardo da Vinci (1452–1519). The sketch from his notebooks reproduced above is probably the first anamorphic drawing.

ANAMORPHICS

Can you identify what is in the picture?

094 2

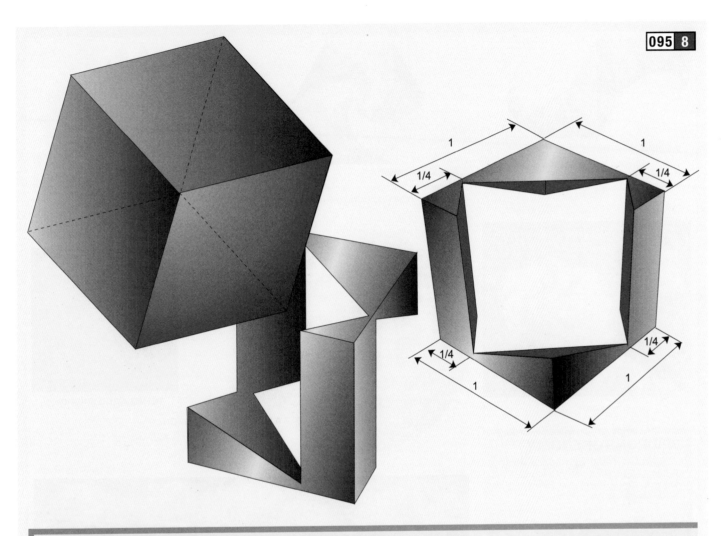

CUBE THROUGH CUBE

PRINCE RUPERT'S PROBLEM

Can you cut a hole through a cube that will enable a bigger cube to pass through it? If you could, what would be the size of a bigger cube that could pass through a smaller cube?

In the 17th century Prince Rupert of the Rhine won a bet that a hole could be made in one of two equal cubes, large enough for the other cube to pass through. A century later Pieter Nieuwland determined the size of the largest cube that can pass through a cube of unit side by finding the largest square that can fit in a cube.

Prince Rupert

Prince Rupert was the nephew of King Charles I of England (r.1625–49). He was the son of Charles's sister Elizabeth who had married Frederick V, Elector of the Palatinate. Rupert was Commander of the Royalist army's cavalry during the English Civil War (1642-51).

A SPIDRON

A planar figure consisting of alternating equilateral and isosceles triangles possessing rotational symmetry – like a polygon of two opposing spirals.

A SPIDRON ARM

Six nested spidrons in a dissected hexagon, which can be folded into an aesthetic three-dimensional relief.

Photo by Regina Markus

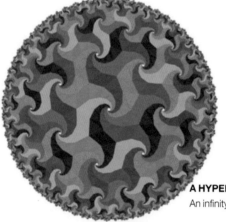

A HYPERBOLIC SPIDRON

An infinity of spidrons by Craig S Kaplan.

TESSELATING SPIDRONS

SPIDRONS OF ERDELY

Playing with triangles, Hungarian industrial designer and artist Daniel Erdely created an amazing three-dimensional world of great mathematical beauty.

In the early 1970s Erdely discovered a new geometrical object, which he called the "spidron." The spidron is essentially a plane structure. Its main feature is its power of folding into complex three-dimensional forms and structures.

The spidron has found a place in a surprisingly diverse variety of mathematical such as plane geometry, tessellations, fractals, dissections, polygons and polyhedra and many other three-dimensional space-filling structures.

This graphic spread is just a small sample of the varieties of spidron structures, showing some of the astonishing work of Erdely and his collaborators Marc Pelletier, Amira Buhler Allen, Walt van Ballegooijen, Craig S Kaplan, Rinus Roelofs, and many others.

photo by Rinus Roelofs

FOLDING SPIDRONS

Three-dimensional sculptural reliefs produced from spidrons can be compressed like an accordion up to a certain limit without bending their individual triangular surfaces, so that only the spatial angles between the faces change.

SPIDRONS 2
THE INFINITE 3-DIMENSIONAL WORLD OF SPIDROHEDRONS

SPIDROHEDRON SCULPTURE

In a park near Leeuwarden, Netherlands. It is a closed polyhedron made of 24 spidrons.

THIRTY COLOR CUBES

Maltese-born mathematician Percy Alexander MacMahon (1854–1929) created a set of 30 color cubes in 1893 that is one of the real gems of recreational mathematics. The set is based on the following problem: If you color each of the six faces of a cube a different color, using the same set of colors for all cubes, how many different cubes can you obtain? Rotations are not considered as different, but reflections are.

I produced the only commercially manufactured set of MacMahon's cubes in 1964 under the name "Cu-Zoo," and it was marketed until 1970. I also created a giant set of 30 color cubes made of soft plastics for the 1969 art exhibition "Play Orbit," at the Institute of Contemporary Art (ICA) in London, where it was handled and enjoyed by small children and adults alike.

Today there is no other way to appreciate the set aside from creating it. But it is well worth the effort as a do-it-yourself project, since the set of cubes is an endless source of fun and puzzles of all levels of difficulty.

How do you to create the set of 30 cubes?

Diagrams of 30 cubes are provided. Can you color (or number) the diagrams using six colors (or numbers from 1 to 6) to create the set? One (tedious) way would be to find all 720 possible permutations of the six colors or numbers. Since you can position a cube in 24 different orientations, there will be 24 appearances of each cube, which gives the number of different cubes as 30. But a better method is to find a way of coloring systematically.

BIG BROTHER

Building a two-by-two-by-two cube model of a selected cube from the set of 30 cubes is the basic MacMahon problem and it is a classic of recreational mathematics.

Select any cube from the set. Use it as a model for creating a larger replica of a two-by-two-by-two cube (from eight cubes), which will be identically colored on its faces, and also match domino-style along the internal touching faces.

MacMahon patented this puzzle under the name "Mayblox" in 1921, and later many variations of the same puzzle were marketed. To find the eight cubes required to solve the puzzle requires a systematic procedure. Don't forget that the total number of ways in which eight cubes can be joined to make a larger cube is 248= 110,075,314,176 – that is, over 110 billion.

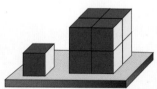

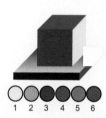

LINEAR CUBES

Can you select six cubes from the set of 30 color cubes and arrange them in a linear fashion as shown, so that six different colors appear in any order on all four sides, and internal faces match, domino-style?

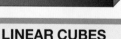

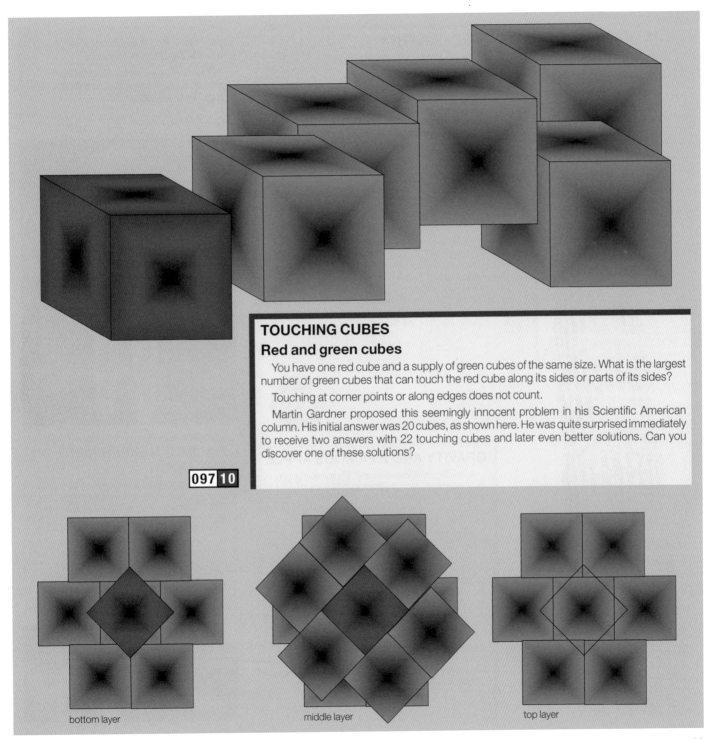

TOUCHING CUBES
Red and green cubes

You have one red cube and a supply of green cubes of the same size. What is the largest number of green cubes that can touch the red cube along its sides or parts of its sides?

Touching at corner points or along edges does not count.

Martin Gardner proposed this seemingly innocent problem in his Scientific American column. His initial answer was 20 cubes, as shown here. He was quite surprised immediately to receive two answers with 22 touching cubes and later even better solutions. Can you discover one of these solutions?

097 10

bottom layer

middle layer

top layer

FREE FALL – GRAVITY
Galileo's Pisa Tower Drop

From very early times people took a great interest in how things fall. To the ancient Greek philosopher Aristotle (385-322BCE), it seemed logical and obvious that heavy objects accelerate faster than lighter ones, in direct proportion to their weights. Nearly 2,000 years later, Italian mathematician Galileo (1564–1642CE) disagreed. Convinced that Aristotle was wrong, he tried to disprove Aristotle's theory by experiment. According to legend, Galileo dropped two objects (cannonballs) of different mass simultaneously from the Leaning Tower of Pisa in northern Italy, demonstrating that their difference in weight made little difference to the rate at which they fell.

But both Aristotle and Galileo made a mistake in comparing the insignificant masses of the two objects, excluding the crucial participating mass of the Earth itself. Only Newton, in his Law of Universal Gravitation, took the mass of the Earth into account.

Newton's law states that the rate of acceleration at which two masses attract each other at a specific distance is proportional to the sum of their masses. Theoretically it should be possible to measure the difference in rates of acceleration. For example, a 2-kilogram (roughly 4lb) mass dropped from a height of about 10 metres (around 30 feet) will accelerate towards the earth faster than a 1-kilogram (roughly 2lb) mass. The heavier mass will strike the ground first, but by a tiny amount – less than the diameter of a nucleus of a hydrogen atom.

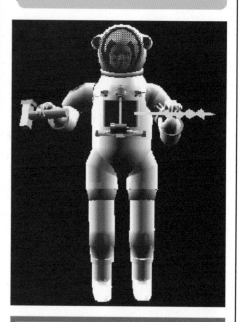

GRAVITY AND A FAMOUS APPLE

According to scientific legend, the force of gravity was discovered by English physicist Isaac Newton (1642-1727) after he saw an apple fall from a tree. What Newton concluded from the incident was that the force that makes the Moon orbit the Earth, and the planets orbit the Sun, is actually the same as the force that makes the apple fall to the ground. How does it do this?

Objects attract each other. Usually, the attraction is so small that it can't be noticed. However, when the object is as big as the Earth, the force is capable of attracting other large objects, even ones as big as the Moon. The Earth is much larger and heavier than the Moon, so the Moon is kept in the Earth's orbit due to gravity. If gravity is capable of keeping the Moon within its orbit, what effect do you think it would have on an itsy-bitsy little apple? It certainly would attract it, and like a magnet attracts a pin – powerfully! Even today, we know only that gravity exists and what it does, but we still don't understand exactly what gravity is or what produces its force.

GALILEO'S EXPERIMENT ON THE MOON

Around 500 years after Galileo, his simple and beautiful experiment was repeated by astronaut David R Scott during the Apollo 15 mission to the Moon in 1971. Scott also released two objects of different mass – a feather and a hammer – simultaneously and both reached the surface of the Moon at the same moment. In this way, finally, he proved the fact that two objects of unequal weights undergoing the same acceleration will fall at the same speed in a vacuum. Galileo was right.

INCLINED PLANE, FREE FALL AND GALILEO'S EXPERIMENTS

Galileo realized that free-fall motion is the key to understanding all types of motion of all bodies. He proposed a simple type of motion that we today call uniform or constant acceleration.

A motion is said to be uniformly accelerated if, when starting from rest, it acquires during equal time intervals equal increments of speed.

If you drop an object from rest from a height h the height is: $h = \frac{1}{2}gt^2$ where t is the time to fall the distance h, and g is the acceleration.

Solving to g gives: $g = 2h/t^2$

In theory it is simple to determine the acceleration of free fall by dropping something and measuring the time it takes to hit the ground. Experimentally, however, this is difficult.

Galileo tried to prove his assumptions by conducting experiments in which he rolled balls down an inclined plane. The movement down the plane was slower than vertical fall – and so easier to measure – but had the same rate of acceleration. Galileo did not have a stop watch: indeed, in his day clocks had no minute (let alone second) hands. Instead he used a pendulum device to measure time.

He released a small ball at the same time as a pendulum swung. At each swing the ball struck a series of adjustable small bells along the inclined plane on its descent. Releasing a ball, Galileo marked its position after exactly 1 second of descent. He then divided the whole length of the inclined plane into units of this length. In a series of experiments he measured the precise position of the ball in unit lengths after 2,3,4,5, and more seconds. By changing the angles of the inclined plane during these experiments Galileo found acceleration to be a constant.

He made some remarkable discoveries. He found that the ratios of the distances increased by odd numbers, and this progression was always the same for any angle: 1, 3, 5, 7, 9, ...

He also found that the total distances covered followed the progression: 1, 4, 9, 16, 25, ...

But, even more remarkably, the distance covered was directly proportional to the square of the time. These discoveries are summarized in the diagram opposite.

INCLINED PLANE – THE PATTERN OF MOTION

How long the ball takes to travel to the end of the plane depends on the plane's inclination, but the ball's speed at the end of the inclined plane does not change. No matter what the inclination, the ball's speed is always the same at the end of the inclined plane.

A ball that rolls a distance down an incline in 1 second, rolls four times as far in 2 seconds, nine times as far in 3 seconds, and 16 times as far in 4 seconds. You can easily test this by rolling a ball on a ruler, provided the angle of incline is sufficiently small, so that the ball will remain rolling for as long as 4 seconds.

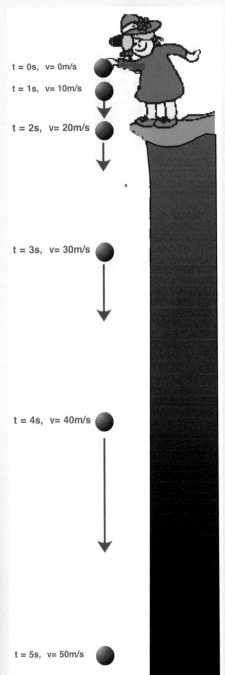

t = 0s, v= 0m/s

t = 1s, v= 10m/s

t = 2s, v= 20m/s

t = 3s, v= 30m/s

t = 4s, v= 40m/s

t = 5s, v= 50m/s

SPEED, VELOCITY, AND ACCELERATION

Understanding speed, velocity and acceleration is fundamental to modern life.

Speed is the distance covered in a unit of time. The units could be km/h or mph, m/s or ft/s (kilometers per hour or miles per hour, meters per second or feet per second). Speed measurements are always relative.

Velocity is the speed of an object in a particular direction. If the speeds of two cars are given it will tell you nothing about whether they will collide, but giving their directions as well will tell you whether they will.

Acceleration is the rate of change of velocity. It tells how quickly an object changes it speed (or velocity) every second. The acceleration due to the Earth's gravitational pull is 10 m/s/s (10 meters per second per second, roughly 32 feet per second per second), which means that an object dropped increases its speed by 10 m/s *every* second it falls until it reaches terminal velocity. In a plane or subway you can only tell that you are moving if your speed changes – in other words when you accelerate.

An object that falls through a vacuum is subjected to only one external force, the gravitational force, expressed as the weight of the object. The weight equation defines the weight W to be equal to the mass m of the object times its gravitational acceleration g:

W = mxg.

The value of g is 9.8 meters per square second (32.2 feet per square second) on the surface of the Earth. For many practical problems, we can assume this factor to be a constant. An object that moves because of the action of gravity alone is said to be "free falling."

The motion of any moving object is described by Newton's Second Law of Motion, force F equals mass m times acceleration a: **F = mxa**. By doing a little simple algebra we can work out the acceleration of an object in terms of the net external force and the mass of the object: **a = F/m**.

For a free-falling object, the net external force is just the weight of the object: **F = W**.

Substituting into the second law equation gives: **a= W/m= (mxg)/m = g**.

The acceleration of an object equals the gravitational acceleration. The mass, size, and shape of the object are not factors in describing its motion. So all objects – regardless of size, shape or weight – free fall with the same acceleration. In a vacuum, a feather falls at the same rate as a hammer. Knowing the acceleration, we can determine the velocity and location of any free-falling object at any time.

The remarkable observation of Galileo that all free-falling objects fall with the same acceleration seems to discover a beautiful simplicity in the laws of nature. But things are not that simple.

The hammer clearly has more mass and weight than the feather and thus experiences a greater pulling force of gravity. But if so, why does it hit the ground at the same times as the feather?

Great question! To answer this question, we must recall Newton's second law – the law of acceleration. Newton's second law states that the acceleration of an object is directly related to the net force and inversely related to its mass. When figuring the acceleration of object, there are two factors to consider – force and mass.

GALILEO

Galileo Galilei (1564-1642CE)

An Italian physicist, mathematician, and astronomer, Galileo was closely associated with the "scientific revolution," a period of science history starting roughly at the mid-16th century. Among his many great achievements is the first systematic study of uniformly accelerated motion. Galileo's experiment-based research was a distinct break from the abstract approach of the Ancient Greek philosopher Aristotle, and is regarded as marking the beginning of experimental science.

Applied to the hammer-feather scenario, we can say that the hammer experiences a much greater force (which tends to produce large accelerations). Yet the mass of an object resists acceleration. Thus, the greater mass of the hammer (which tends to produce small accelerations) offsets the influence of the greater force. It is the force/mass ratio that determines the acceleration. Even though the hammer may experience 1000 times the force of a feather, it has 1000 times the mass. The force/mass ratio is the same for each. The greater mass of the hammer requires the greater force just to maintain the same acceleration as the feather.

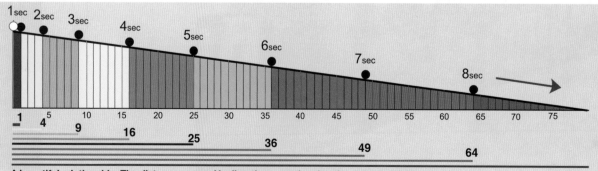

A beautiful relationship: The distance covered is directly proportional to the square of time.

PARALLELOGRAM OF FORCES AND INCLINED PLANES

A beautiful method of calculating forces

Beginning in the 1580s with the work of Simon Stevin (1548-1620) and Galileo Galilei, many engineers transformed the principles of mechanics into mathematical form. Often, that translation involved devising abstract mathematical models of the physical mechanisms and the mechanism of parallelogram of forces is an example. In mathematics and physics a parallelogram of forces is the ingenious method of calculating the combined effort (resultant) of two or more forces acting together on an object.

In physics, a tilted surface is called an inclined plane. It is important to analyze the forces acting upon an object on an inclined plane. In our diagram the two forces acting on the sides of the inclined plane are vectors acting from a point. Their size is the sum of the weights of the small metal spheres acting on the inclined plane. These forces (black) represent the force of gravity (also known as the weight) acting in a downward direction. But there are always at least two forces acting upon any object that is on an inclined plane. The other force is the normal force (blue) always acting in a direction perpendicular to the surface. Using the parallelogram of forces, the force of gravity is resolved into two components of force: one directed parallel to the inclined surface and the other directed perpendicular to the inclined surface.

A **force** is a *vector quantity*. Since a force has both a magnitude and direction, it can be conveniently represented by a directed straight line.

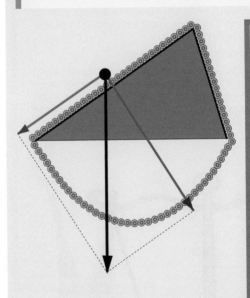

STEVIN'S "WREATH OF SPHERES"

Dutch mathematician and engineer Simon Stevin (1548–1620) is best known for his contribution to statics (the science of forces under equilibrium) and hydrostatics. His most famous discovery was the Law of Inclined Planes, which he proved by drawing his famous "wreath of spheres" illustration, featured as the title page of *The Elements of the Art of Weighing* in 1615.

Stevin's law of forces on inclined planes, and more generally his vector law for the decomposition of forces (also known as the parallelogram of forces) is noteworthy as a thought experiment, because it is one of the first and early examples of a law of mechanics deduced from a general physical principle, the conservation of energy.

His problem was to determine the force **F** required to hold a frictionless object (of a known weight **W**) in place on a frictionless inclined plane as shown above.

The basic premise of his law is that less weight on a steep slope can

balance more weight on a gentler slope.

He approached the problem by the thought experiment of his "wreath of spheres," which was a double inclined plane around which a loop of small connected spheres was placed, as shown.

He reasoned that when the loop of the chain below the slopes is removed nothing changes – everything stays in equilibrium. (Otherwise he would have had "something that moves," which would be a perpetual motion machine.) So by leaving out the "free" spheres hanging in the air, the system remains in equilibrium. In this way he realized that when weights are in equilibrium on the inclined planes, the weights of the bodies involved are proportional to the lengths of the planes. He just had to count the number of small spheres on both sides of the inclined planes, and he had the proof of his law! His beautiful geometrical argument with the necklace of small metal spheres acting as weights was right.

Stevin was so proud of his discovery that he wrote on his frontispiece the sentence, which became later his motto: *"Wonder en is gheen wonder"* ("What appears a wonder is not a wonder").

Equilibrium on the slopes was due to the relationship between the

downward forces on either side, due to the differing angles of their support. Such a decomposition of forces is known today as the parallelogram of forces, visually demonstrated in bigger detail (left).

PUZZLE 1

If weights are allowed on only one side of the scales, can you work out both the minimum number of different weights and the proper distribution of weights you will need to weigh 1 to 40 kilograms of sugar?

PUZZLE 2

If weights are allowed on both sides of the scales, can you work out both the minimum number of different weights and the proper distribution of weights you will need to weigh 1 to 40 kilograms of sugar?

C. G. DE MEZIRIAC 1635.

BACHET'S WEIGHTS PROBLEM

Bachet's Book

In 1612 French scholar Claude-Gaspar Bachet de Meziriac published a collection of puzzles entitled Problèmes plaisants et délectables qui se font les nombres ("Amusing and Delightful Number Problems"). Bachet's emphasis was on arithmetical rather than geometrical problems. His book was the inspiration for all later books on recreational mathematics.

His book included a classic Weights problem:

"Suppose you need to weigh any weight of sugar from 1 to 40 pounds on the scales shown. Can you work out the minimum number of weights you would need to have if: (1) the weights can be placed on only one side of the scales; and (2) if the weights can be placed on both sides of the scales?"

1	=
2	=
3	=
4	=
5	=
6	=
7	=
8	=
9	=
10	=
11	=
12	=
13	=
14	=
15	=
16	=
17	=
18	=
19	=
20	=
21	=
22	=
23	=
24	=
25	=
26	=
27	=
28	=
29	=
30	=
31	=
32	=
33	=
34	=
35	=
36	=
37	=
38	=
39	=
40	=

1	=
2	=
3	=
4	=
5	=
6	=
7	=
8	=
9	=
10	=
11	=
12	=
13	=
14	=
15	=
16	=
17	=
18	=
19	=
20	=
21	=
22	=
23	=
24	=
25	=
26	=
27	=
28	=
29	=
30	=
31	=
32	=
33	=
34	=
35	=
36	=
37	=
38	=
39	=
40	=

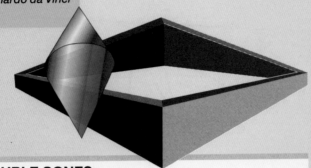

099 6

ANTI-GRAVITY DOUBLE CONES

Can an object defy gravity? Galileo devised many ingenious mechanical experimental devices, among them the simple device shown in the illustration above.

Can you anticipate and explain what will happen when you place his double cone on the double tracks at their lowest points at one of the ends and release it?

The answer, surprisingly, is that the double cone will start rolling up the double track towards their higher ends. How can you explain this paradoxical phenomenon? Is the double cone really rolling uphill?

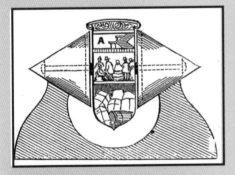

ANTI-GRAVITY RAILWAY

A self-moving railway carriage concept

The fascinating behavior of the anti-gravity cones of Galileo inspired a Victorian inventor in 1829 to conceive the concept of the antigravity railway based on its principle of motion.

CENTER OF GRAVITY

You cannot actually see the invisible point that is the center of gravity of every object – but it is there. It is the point at which we can imagine the total weight of a body is concentrated and acts. In a simple sphere it is at its center. In other irregular bodies it can be anywhere, even outside of it. The center of gravity of an object tends to occupy the lowest position if possible in which unstable equilibrium becomes stable.

ANTIGRAVITY
THE UNIVERSE AND EINSTEIN

In 1907 German-born physicist Albert Einstein (1879–1955) was sitting in his office when the thought occurred to him, "If a person falls freely he will not feel his own weight." As he later recounted it, this was the happiest thought of his life and led to his greatest accomplishment. The falling person was Einstein's version of the apple that inspired English physicist Isaac Newton (1643–1727), and the idea that led to a new theory of gravitation, substituting Newton's theory of gravity.

The concept of antigravity is associated with the biggest scientific issue of all – the origin of the universe. When Einstein developed general relativity (his theory of gravity) he became aware of a tricky problem. Why had gravity not caused the matter in the universe to collapse inwards on itself? Newton had been confronted with the same problem with his own theory of gravity, and had answered it by explaining that God was responsible for keeping things apart. Einstein was reluctant to invoke God: his solution was to propose the existence of an antigravity force that operated alongside gravity.

In the 1920s all that changed. Cosmologists developed a new view, according to which the universe came into being at a finite moment, exploding with immense force from a small primeval superatom and expanding ever since, a view that developed into the "Big Bang theory." The theory did not require the belief in antigravity. It seemed to be correct and Einstein eventually endorsed it.

But there is a twist to the tale. The expansion of the Big Bang should be slowing, because of the effects of gravity, but to their astonishment, astronomers found that the universe is accelerating and galaxies are moving apart faster and faster all the time. Once again, there was a problem. The best explanation was the existence of an antigravity force.

Simon Singh, author of Big Bang: The Origins of the Universe, notes that even when Einstein thought he was wrong, and was prepared to admit it, he turned out to be right. Perhaps humility, more than anything, is the mark of true genius.

CHANCE BALANCE

How many ways can you find to arrange the five weights so that the scale is in equilibrium when you remove the two cylindrical supports? Remember that the further a weight is from the fulcrum, the more force it exerts. So a weight over the number 2 on the scale would exert twice as much force as the same weight over the number 1. If you place the weights at random on the scale, what is the probability that they will be in equilibrium?

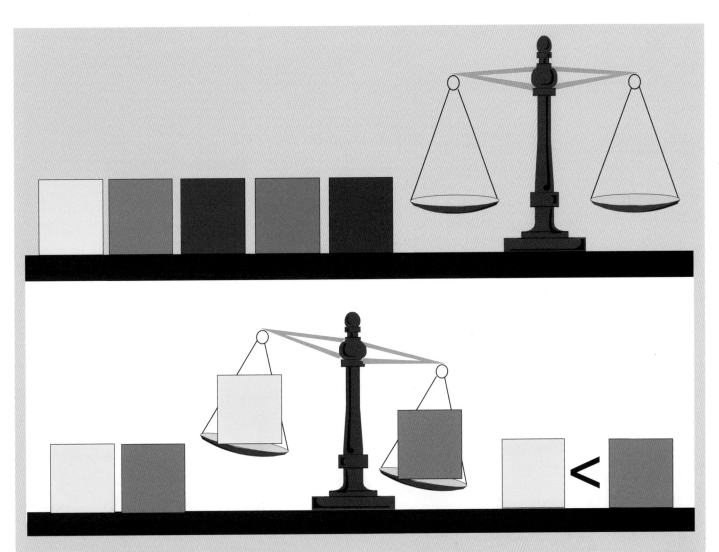

101 8

WEIGHT RANKING

You have been asked to rank a number of given objects in order of increasing weight, using a balance scale but no weights. For two objects one weighing is enough, as shown. What is the minimal number of weighing for three, four, and five weights?

131

PENDULUM
In the swing of things

Pendulums have fascinated scientists for centuries. A pendulum can keep time, measure the force of gravity, and sense relative motion. Italian scientist Galileo (1564–1642) realized that a pendulum swings for (almost) the same period whether it has a small or a large swing. With this simple observation he invented the pendulum clock. The mass of the bob does not matter; but as the length is increased the period lengthens by the square root of the length of the pendulum.

In places where gravity is weaker – such as on the top of mountains or on the Moon – pendulums are slower. And a pendulum on a massive planet such as Jupiter – where gravity is stronger – would swing faster.

But if a pendulum swings faster under stronger gravitational pull, why does a heavier bob not swing faster than a light bob? The reason is that the increased inertia of the heavier bob requires more force to accelerate it, and the extra force required is exactly the same as the increased gravitational attraction. This means that inertia and gravity are precisely related. For English physicist Isaac Newton (1643–1727) this exact relationship was a total mystery. It was to him too much of a coincidence, and yet there was no visible or conceptual link between inertia and gravity to explain it.

This was one of the questions that led German-born physicist Albert Einstein (1879–1955) to theorize that inertia and gravity are ultimately the same. But to say this he had to create a new picture of the Universe – and then persuade his fellow physicists to follow him, which they ultimately did.

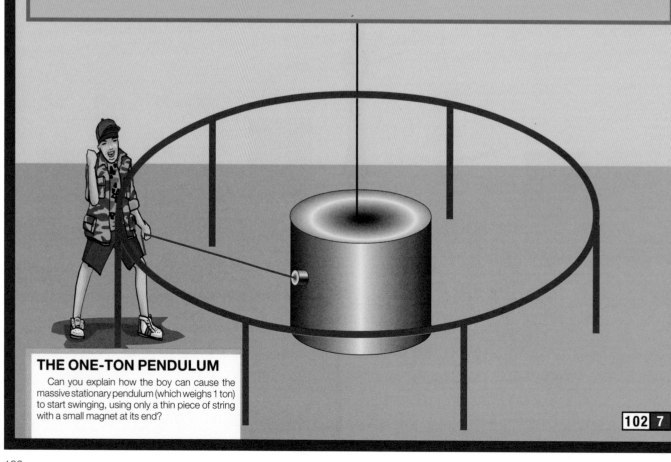

THE ONE-TON PENDULUM

Can you explain how the boy can cause the massive stationary pendulum (which weighs 1 ton) to start swinging, using only a thin piece of string with a small magnet at its end?

FOUCAULT PENDULUM

How do you know that the Earth moves?

Astronomers from the time of Ancient Greek philosopher Plato (428–328BCE) up until the 16th century CE tended to think that the Earth was stationary and everything else rotated around it. Theories contradicting this view were not lacking but the problem was that convincing evidence was hard to find.

We certainly cannot feel that we are on a moving platform. Can we see that the Earth is moving? Is it possible to watch the Earth rotate?

In 1543 Polish astronomer Nicolaus Copernicus (1473–1543) sent a copy of his book On the Revolutions of the Celestial Orbs to Pope Paul III with a note containing the famous understatement, "I can easily conceive that as soon as people learn that in this book I ascribe certain motions to the earth, they will cry out at once that I and my theory should be rejected." Some still disbelieved the theory when the French physicist Jean-Bernard Foucault (1819–68) was invited to arrange a scientific exhibit as part of the Paris Exhibition in 1851. From the dome of the Pantheon, Foucault hung a pendulum consisting of 61 meters (200 feet) of piano wire and a 27-kilogram (60lb) cannonball. On the floor below the ball, he sprinkled a layer of fine sand. A stylus fixed to the bottom of the ball traced the path in the sand, thus recording the movement of the pendulum.

At the end an hour, the line in the sand had moved 11 degrees and 18 minutes. This could be explained only on the basis that the Earth had turned beneath the pendulum. The Foucault pendulum demonstration was certainly one of the most impressive scientific demonstrations ever, and still is, when it is recreated at science museums and science exhibitions all over the world.

But how does it work? If the pendulum stays in the same plane, how can it trace different paths in the sand?

103 **8**

MOONWALK PHOTO

On his giant high-resolution TV screen my neighbor, who is a former astronaut, proudly showed me this dramatic photograph, which he took of his friend, a fellow-astronaut, on the Moon. What is wrong with his photograph?

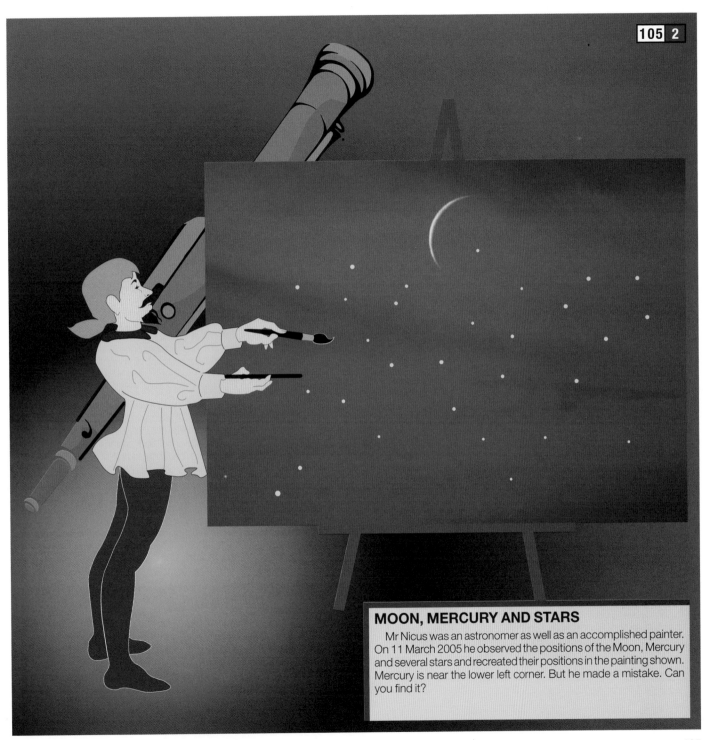

MOON, MERCURY AND STARS

Mr Nicus was an astronomer as well as an accomplished painter. On 11 March 2005 he observed the positions of the Moon, Mercury and several stars and recreated their positions in the painting shown. Mercury is near the lower left corner. But he made a mistake. Can you find it?

> "I do not suppose there is anyone who has not occasionally blown a common soap bubble, and while admiring the perfection of its form, and the marvellous brilliancy of its colors, wondered how it is that such a magnificent object can be so easily produced. I hope that none of you are tired of playing with bubbles, because there is more in a common bubble than those who have only played with them generally imagine."

Victorian science writer Charles V Boys, famous from his lecture series for children at the London Institution, in 1902. He is also celebrated for his fantastic book *Soap Bubbles and the Forces Which Mould Them).*

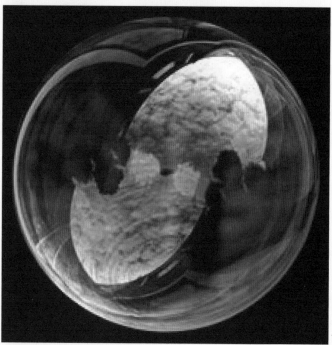

SOAP BUBBLES

You might think soap bubbles were far removed from serious science and mathematics. But you'd be wrong. Scientists study bubbles to get answers to some of the most profound questions of nature.

One of their main aims in investigating bubbles is to learn how to build structures using the smallest amount of building material.

Why are soap bubbles round?

Because surface tension makes the surface contract as much as possible. Soap bubbles form a sphere because this shape encloses a given volume with a minimum amount of surface. The sphere is the geometric solid that has the least surface area for the same volume.

For the same reason, most drops of water become spherical. Molecules far from the surface of a liquid can be attracted in all directions, but the ones near the surface will be pulled back into the liquid by other molecules. This attraction creates a tendency to minimize the surface area, which becomes as small as possible and behaves like an elastic film. This is surface tension.

Soap has a tendency to reduce the surface tension of water, which is the reason it can pull molecules from a body of water to create spherical soap bubbles or soap films. Soap films are examples of "minimal surfaces," as nature selects the shape that requires the minimal amount of total energy to maintain.

MINIMAL SURFACE, MAXIMUM SIZE

Tim blows a giant bubble in his courtyard. This one was big, but not big enough to be a record breaker. The Guinness Book of Records lists a 15-meter (50-foot) bubble as the biggest ever.

PLATEAU'S PROBLEM
Soap structures, honeycombs, and minimal surfaces

Soap films are used for demonstrations of laws of calculus, as they almost instantly stretch across wire frames to form the single minimal surface connected to the frame – the surface that has the smallest possible area.

The problem of finding the minimal routes (the smallest number of rorutes) between a number of points is extremely challenging. But simple wire models dipped into soap solution often give complex solutions in no time.

When doing such simple experiments we should be aware that we are dealing with problems in the domain of the "calculus of variations," a difficult field of mathematics. Can you guess what the minimal routes interconnecting two, three, four, five, and six points will look like?

Why do all bees build their honeycombs around the same form – the regular hexagon?

The hexagonal form of a honeycomb contains the greatest amount of honey with the least amount of beeswax and is the form that requires the smallest amount of energy for the bees to construct.

It is no accident that honeycomb cells have regular hexagonal shapes. The shape of the cells must enable three or more of them to fit together at a corner adding up the angles to 360 degrees at all corners. The only regular polygons that would serve this purpose are: equilateral triangles, squares, or regular hexagons. (No regular polygons with more than six sides can do, because then each angle would contain more than 120 degrees, and three or more of them could not possibly fit together around a point.) Of these three possibilities, the regular hexagon is the best, because it stores the most honey between the walls of wax.

The regular hexagon is a minimal structure, a perfect construction form. Many modern man-made structures are being built from hexagonal cells, resulting in strength and economy. An example is the revolutionary geodesic dome devised by US inventor Buckminster Fuller (1895–1983).

`106` `8`

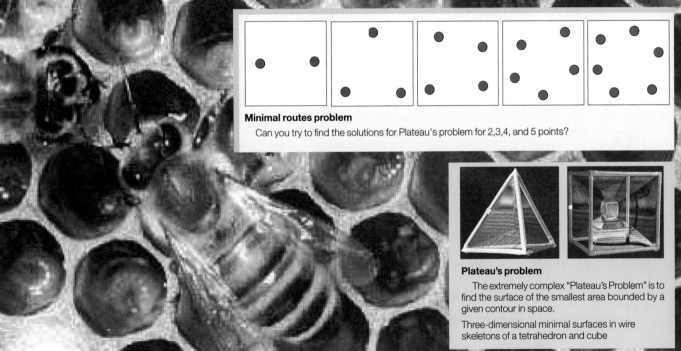

Minimal routes problem

Can you try to find the solutions for Plateau's problem for 2,3,4, and 5 points?

Plateau's problem

The extremely complex "Plateau's Problem" is to find the surface of the smallest area bounded by a given contour in space.

Three-dimensional minimal surfaces in wire skeletons of a tetrahedron and cube

137

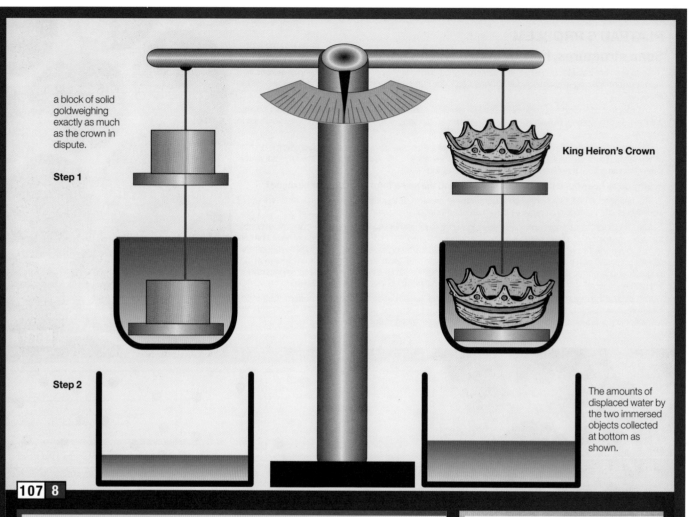

a block of solid gold weighing exactly as much as the crown in dispute.

Step 1

King Heiron's Crown

Step 2

The amounts of displaced water by the two immersed objects collected at bottom as shown.

ARCHIMEDES' PRINCIPLE

According to legend, Sicilian mathematician Archimedes (c.287–212 BCE) was so excited when he discovered the principle of hydrostatics that he leapt naked from his bathtub and ran into the street shouting "Eureka!" ("I've found it!")

He was attempting to work out a way of proving the suspicion that a new crown ordered by King Hieron of Syracuse was not solid gold but also contained other materials. He solved the problem without melting down the crown, by discovering the principle named today after him: one can determine the density of an object (O), by comparing its weight to that of the water it displaces.

Step 1 Archimedes found a block of gold that weighed exactly the same as the disputed crown.

Step 2 He weighed both objects immersed in water and measured the water displaced by both objects, as shown.

What was Archimedes conclusion from this experiment?

"EUREKA!" MOMENTS

There are many other recorded instances of creative "lightning flashes" like that experienced by Archimedes. Scottish mechanical engineer James Watt (1736–1819) was struck with the idea of the steam engine while watching his kettle boil; Hungarian-American physicist Leó Szilárd had a sudden illumination of a neutron chain reaction (or how to make an atomic bomb) while waiting at traffic lights.

MIXING MARBLES AND TEA WITH MILK

One of the most beautiful – and counterintuitive – puzzles I have ever encountered is question about mixing milk and tea. A person adds a teaspoon of milk to a cup of tea, and then adds a teaspoon of the mixture (of milk and tea) to the cup of milk: afterwards, is there more milk in the tea than tea in the milk or more tea in the milk than milk in the tea?

The answer is that there is exactly the same amount of milk in the tea as tea in the milk.

The explanation is that the total volume in each glass is unchanged by the transfers; the net volume transferred from cup A (milk) to cup B (tea), exactly cancels that which goes from cup B to cup A. Initially I was a bit sceptical about this answer, but many years later I performed an analogous experiment involving marbles in two colors instead of tea and milk, which you can easily repeat. Try it – you'll be convinced.

Take two boxes filled with marbles, let's say 50 marbles in each box, one box with red marbles and the other green – as shown. Take five marbles from the red box and transfer them to the green box. Mix the green box well and return five randomly selected marbles to the red box.

The experiment is presented visually, below right. There are six possible ways to return the marbles back into the red box. In each case there is the same amount of wrong color in each box. Check! The same will always happen no matter how many marbles are transferred.

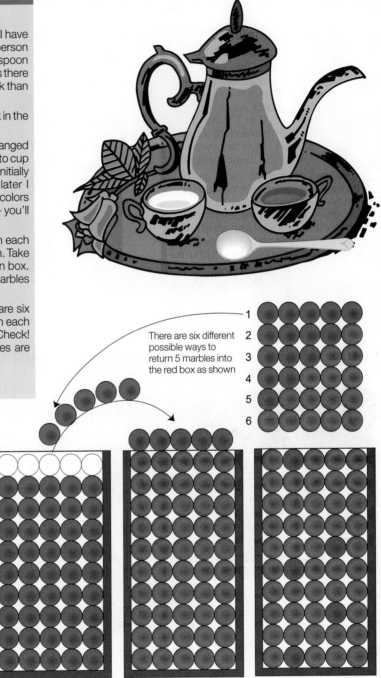

There are six different possible ways to return 5 marbles into the red box as shown

Transferring 5 marbles into the green box

Mixing the green box

The Shuttle spacecraft docks into the Russian space station *Mir*

THE BEAUTIFUL ANCIENT DREAM OF FLYING

From earliest times humans looked upwards and longed to fly. Myths and legends tell us many stories of flying men.

1 The ancient Greek myth of Daedalus and Icarus is one of the most celebrated of these early tales.

2 Italian artist and inventor Leonardo da Vinci (1452-1519) designed several flying machines, of which his helicopter concept is perhaps the most ingenious.

3 The Montgolfier brothers, Joseph-Michel (1740-1810) and Jacques-Etienne (1745-99) invented the first practical hot air balloon. The first manned flight took place on 21 November 1783 in Paris, France.

4 Frenchman Clement Ader (1841-1906) built a steam airplane, the Eole, which was the first heavier-than-air airplane to launch a human being into the air. On 9 October 1890, Ader flew the *Eole* for 50 meters (160 feet) at a height of 20 centimeters (8 inches).

5 The Wright Brothers Wilbur (1867-1912) and Orville (1871-1948) in 1904, Ferdinand Ferber (1862-1909) in 1905, Alberto Santos-Dumont (1973-1932) in 1906: all flew in their turn and the air was conquered.

6 After conquering the air, humans turned to space. The old dreams were upstaged. Yuri Gagarin (1934-68) in the Soviet spacecraft Vostok 1 on 12 April 1961, and one month later American Alan Shepard (1923-98) in Freedom 7 on 5 May, were the first humans in space. Neil Armstrong and Buzz Aldrin (both born 1930) took the first steps on the Moon on 20 July 1969. These were only the first steps in a journey of leaving Earth, which will take humans into an unknown and exciting "New Frontier."

HOW AIRPLANES FLY

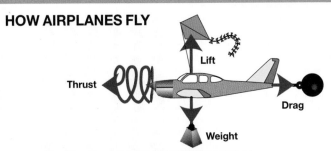

Four basic aerodynamic forces play a role in flight: lift, thrust, weight, and drag.

For level flight thrust (by propeller, jet engine, or rocket) is greater than drag. Lift is the aerodynamic force that holds an airplane in the air, most of which is created by the wings.

Lift is the trickiest force to explain, without using a great deal of complex math related to the fact that air is a fluid and behaves in similar manner to water and other liquids. It is a rich and beautiful math, involving curvature, angle, symmetry, and pattern.

Simplified explanations of how airplanes fly in high-school textbooks and popular literature avoid the complex math. They are often flawed and, at best, provide no more than an intuitive understanding of the principles of flight.

The two main simplified explanations used to explain lift are:
• the Longer Path or Bernoulli effect; and
• the Newtonian, or Air deflection Principle.

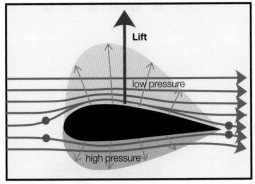

The Longer Path Explanation

This states that the top surface of a wing is more curved than the bottom surface. Air particles reaching the leading edge of the wing travel either over or under the wing, so two nearby particles split and meet again at the trailing edge of the wing. The top particle goes over a longer distance than the lower one in the same amount of time, so must be traveling faster.

Bernoulli's equation, a basic of fluid mechanics, states that as a fluid's rate of flow increases its pressure decreases. There is a lower pressure on the top surface of the wing and a higher pressure on the wing's bottom surface. This pressure difference pushes the wing upward, creating lift.

This is a very common explanation found in high-school textbooks and even encyclopedias, but it is not fully correct and not sufficient. The reasons are several. There is no logical reason for the two split particles to meet at the rear of the wing. Moreover many wings are symmetrical (the wing's top surface is not more curved than its bottom surface). What's more, the explanation excludes the possibility of an airplane flying upside down – and we know that many airplanes can do that.

A common depiction of airflow over a wing is shown below (left). This wing has no lift. In order to generate the required lift for a small airplane the distance over the top of the wing must be about 50 per cent longer than under the bottom, and an airfoil like that would look the right-hand illustration.

A small airplane would have to fly at more than 650km/h (400 mph) to generate enough lift to fly. Clearly something is wrong with the Longer Path explanation!

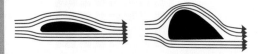

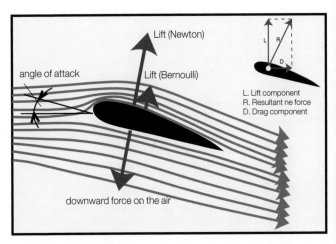

The Newtonian explanation

English physicist Isaac Newton (1642-1727) stated that for every action there is an equal and opposite reaction. (This is Newton's Third Law). According to the Newtonian explanation of flight, molecules behave like shotgun pellets hitting the bottom surface of a wing: they are deflected downward, and impart some of their momentum to the wing. Every molecular impact pushes the wing upward.

This explanation is not entirely correct. At low speeds molecules interact and don't really behave like pellets striking the wing. However, at hypersonic speeds Newtonian theory holds true.

The Bernoulli effect gives some lift, but it is not the primary force keeping the plane aloft. The primary source of lift on an airplane wing is the Newton's third law reaction to the downward force on the air.

The net force of lift is created by pressure differences on all points around the wing and is the result of contributions from both the top and bottom wing surfaces.

The lift of a wing is proportional to the amount of air diverted down times the downward velocity of that air – as simple as that!

PERCEPTION AND OPTICAL ILLUSIONS

The Limits of Seeing

We have five senses through which we perceive the world around us: seeing, hearing, touching, tasting, and smelling. These senses are not perfect and can sometimes fool us. Our brains have the job of interpreting the messages our senses send in, but some messages are misinterpreted so that we get a misleading impression of what is happening outside us.

A movie film only appears to show movement. We know that the pictures on the film are perfectly still but we fool our brains into believing that we see actual movement when the still pictures are shown in quick succession.

Most people experience seeing as a passive process. But in fact perception is an active, pattern-seeking process closely allied to the act of thinking. The brain is as much a seeing organ as the eye. Perception is a creative act.

Among the most interesting perceptual phenomena are optical illusions or, as they are sometimes called "geometrical paradoxes." Optical illusions take advantage of the tendency of the human brain to see things as it thinks they should be – based on previous similar experiences – rather than as they are.

Optical illusions have been studied for thousands of years, and put to practical uses. In the mid-5th century BCE, the ancient Greeks incorporated a slight convexity in the columns of the Parthenon temple in Athens to compensate for the illusion of concavity created by parallel lines. They built the columns slightly misshapen so they would "look right."

We can be made to believe things are larger than they are, to see depth in a two-dimensional flat surface, to see colors where there aren't any, and to see motion where there isn't any.

Our visual system can even operate with limited information. It "fills in" where there are gaps. Much of art is based on this tendency to fill in, to complete, and to organize.

The ease with which we can be fooled by a simple optical illusion should be a warning about the general unreliability of our observation. (Remember that, if you should ever have to listen to eyewitness testimony.) There is a limit to the reliability of our senses, and no amount of practice can ever make them good enough for some special tasks.

One solution to this problem is to find ways to extend our senses, to invent devices capable of perceiving and recording information without error. Although no one has created a perfect system for doing this, cameras and recorders have proven to be much more reliable and free from bias than even the best human observer.

I have selected some of the most baffling, surprising and beautiful optical illusions. They do magic and tricks with color, size, shapes, and movement that will make you wonder whether seeing really is believing.

108 5

PERCEPTION, ART AND ILLUSION

Our brains are marvellously adept at seeing relationships between images or at seeing the same images in different ways. Our perceptions are based on illusions, and they sometimes deceive us. Yet without this capacity we would never be able to make sense of the three-dimensional world.

How else would we "see" that according to the rules of perspective on the two-dimensional plane of the page the first four sculptures from the left are the same size and the sculpture at the right is the biggest?

As our civilization progressed, we learned increasingly through the medium of flat sheets of paper, flat chalkboards and flat screens. We have become so used to seeing a two-dimensional image as a three-dimensional object that this transformation has become an automatic part of perception.

How many different-sized sculptures are really there?

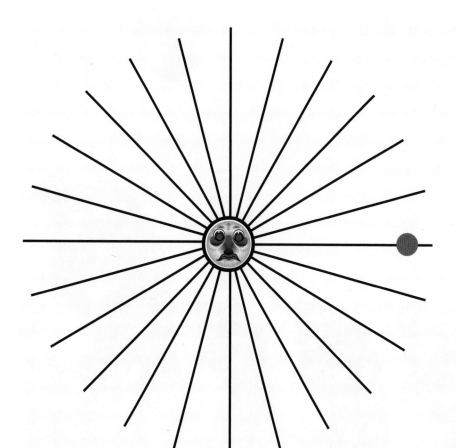

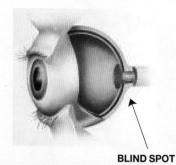

BLIND SPOT

BLIND SPOT

Just by looking can you make the circle with the face disappear?

The brain is extremely good at filling in empty holes, helping us to see. Thus, paradoxically, we can conclude "nothing as such cannot exist".

To see the effects of the blind spot, close your right eye and gaze at the red dot on the right with your left eye. At a certain distance, the circle should disappear. However, you still don't just see a hole instead. The lines appear to be continuous.

Research shows that when the incomplete signal from the eye reaches the brain, the brain uses simple rules to calculate what the blind spot of the retina should be seeing. In this case it extrapolates the lines, and deduces that there is a pattern of radial lines from a center, and so it simply fills the gap. A number of puzzles use this phenomenon to make things disappear.

THE SCIENCE OF THE BLIND SPOT

The disappearance of the face at a certain distance is sudden and striking. The blind spot phenomenon demonstrates that you can't see everything, nor can you really trust your eyes!

One eye does not cover the entire visual field. There are no visual receptors over an area of about 1.5 mm in diameter, where the optic nerve enters the retina. The 17th century French scientist Edme Mariotte discovered that the optic disc (the small area of the retina where the optic nerve attaches to the eyeball) is not sensitive to light. He deduced that the eye is blind at that spot. Actually we have two blind spots, one in each eye. It is interesting to note that the blind spot for one eye is located slightly differently to the blind spot in the other one, which means that in normal activities you don't notice it because each eye sees what the blind spot in the other eye does not.

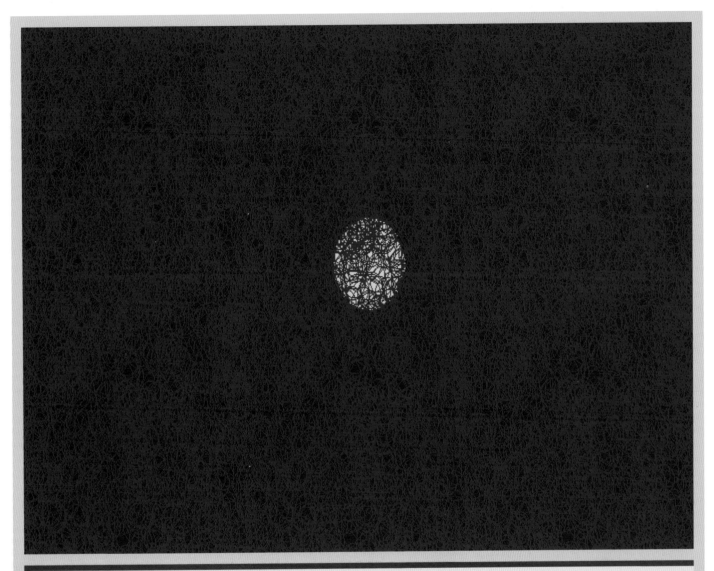

HOLE IN THE WALL

Most visual illusions are based on faults in the human visual system that affect all viewers similarly. But the illusion above is perceived differently by different viewers.

The figure consists of a blue background onto which a great number of small randomly placed circles are densely scattered. In the middle a yellow oval background is placed.

Around 70 per cent of viewers see the light circle as floating above the rest, while 20 per cent see the yellow oval behind the background. The other 10 per cent of viewers do not perceive any effects of depth at all. It is even more striking that the illusion strongly intensifies when one moves back from the figure.

CONTRAST ILLUSION – HOW MANY SHADES ARE THERE?

In the top row we can see eight shades of reds, at the bottom only four. Nothing has changed, except that we have covered the dividing lines with pencils. There are still the same eight shades there. How can you explain the illusion?

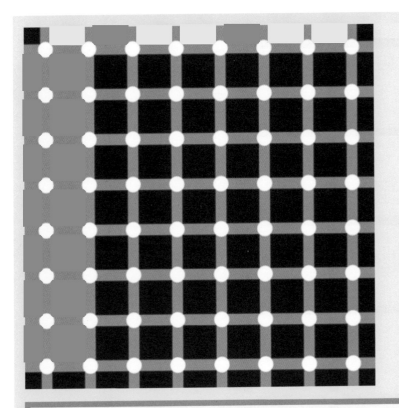

110 1

AFTERIMAGE SPOTS

Our brain can make us "see" things that are not there. How many black dots can you count at the intersections of the pattern of black squares above? And in the patterns on the right, how many red, green, and blue spots can you see even though they're not there?

AFTERIMAGES

An afterimage or ghost image is an optical illusion. The term refers to an image continuing to appear in one's vision after the exposure to the original image has ceased. Afterimages come in two forms, negative (inverted) and positive (retaining the original color).

Negative afterimages are caused when your eye's photoreceptors, primarily those known as cone cells, are over-stimulated and lose sensitivity. When you then divert your eyes to a blank space, the over-stimulated photoreceptors send out little signal and those colors remain muted. However, the surrounding cones that were not being excited by that color are still "fresh," and send out a strong signal. The signal is exactly the same as if you were looking at the opposite color, which is how the brain interprets it. Positive afterimages, by contrast, appear in the same color as the original image. They are often very brief, lasting less than half a second, and may not occur unless the stimulus is very bright. The cause of positive afterimages is not well known.

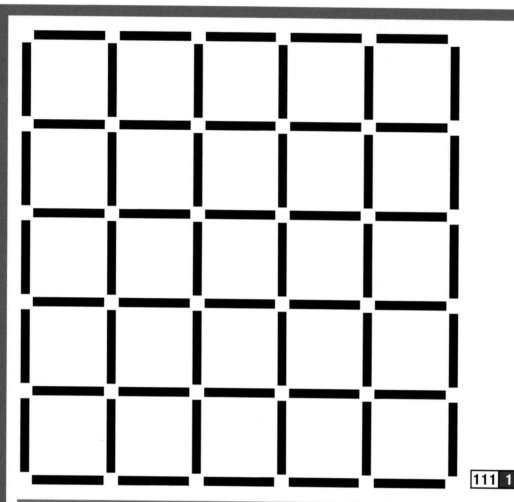

111 1

SUBJECTIVE CONTOURS AND ILLUSORY SQUARES
Whiter than White

At the intersections of the thick black lines we "see" complete white squares that seem lighter than the background. The illusion is quite striking.

In the smaller artwork (right), we see a solid square even though there are only four three-quarter circles. But if you cover any two corners of the square, the square will disappear. Why?

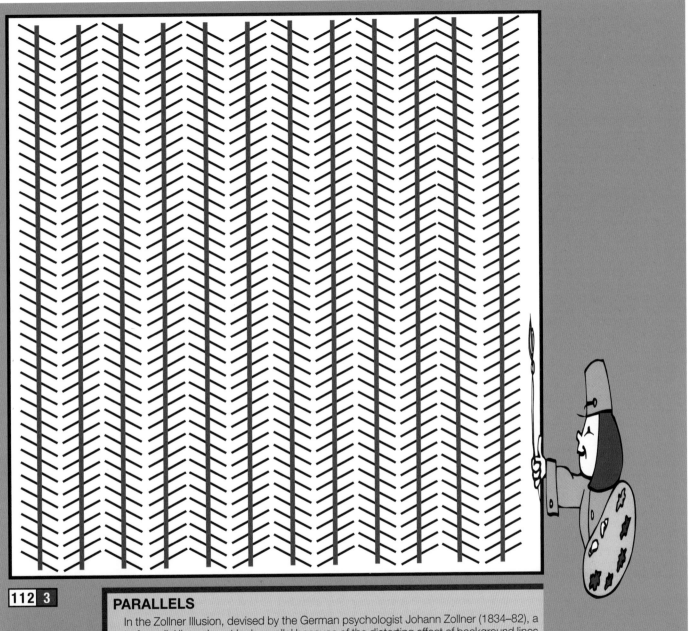

PARALLELS

In the Zollner Illusion, devised by the German psychologist Johann Zollner (1834–82), a set of parallel lines do not look parallel because of the distorting effect of background lines intersecting the parallel lines at acute angles (10–30 degrees).

Our illusion is a slightly modified Zollner illusion. Some lines are parallel, some are not. Can you tell which are which?

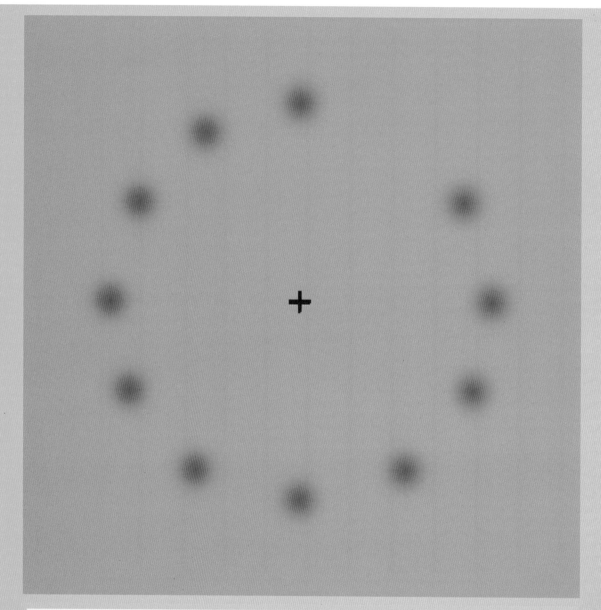

COLOR AFTERIMAGES
Created by Jeremy L Hinton as "LILAC CHASER"

Fix your eyes on the cross in the center. The colored spots will disappear in a few seconds, due to an effect called "retinal fatigue," which occurs when the afterimage of an object cancels the stimulus of the object on the retina. But after a while you will also see green afterimages appearing.

PERSPECTIVE
Relativity of magnitude

Perspective is a representation on a flat surface of an image as it is perceived by the eye. Perspective as we know it in western art is extraordinarily recent – it dates only from the Italian Renaissance in the 15th century. In all known primitive art, and in the art of all previous civilizations, there is no use of perspective. In the highly developed formalized paintings of the ancient Egyptians, heads and feet are shown in profile, never foreshortened by perspective – which gives the figures a resemblance to children's art.

As developed by the 15th-century draftsmen, perspective is a set of rules that enables the artist to convey the illusion of three-dimensional space on a two-dimensional plane by making structural lines converge at an imaginary "vanishing point" on an imaginary horizon at the viewer's level.

It is an extraordinary fact that simple geometrical perspective took so long to develop – far longer than fire or the wheel – and yet in a sense it has always been present for seeing.

The laws and principles of perspective were first clearly described by Italian painter and engineer Leonardo da Vinci (1452-1519). He treated perspective as branch of geometry, describing how perspective could be drawn directly on a sheet of glass. This technique was used by the 17th-century artists known as the "Dutch masters."

Perspective allows you to cover the distant sun with your outstretched hands or even hold it in your hands.

THE ARTIST'S GLASS
The artist's glass was devised by Leon Battista Alberti (1404-72) and used by Leonardo da Vinci for drawing images in perspective. This illustration of the device is by German printmaker Albrecht Dürer (1471-1528).

ANITTA AS A GIANT
Anitta is visiting Medurodam, the Dutch miniature city.

UPSIDE DOWN

upside down

UPSIDE DOWN

One of the astonishing and beautiful "Inversions" of Scott Kim. Turn the page upside-down.

113 3

WINE GLASS ON A TRAY

Do you think the wine glass is on the tray? A striking and surprising optical illusion by Gianni A. Sarcone, as it appeared in the INFINITY magazine published by Tarquin publications.

CONVEX – CONCAVE

Perception relies to a great extent on our using assumptions about the world to resolve ambiguities. We make sense of a shaded picture depending on where we think the light is coming from. The light usually comes from an overhead source of light. How can you change the direction of light in the picture?

UPSIDE-DOWN WORLD – MAGIC AND ILLUSIONS

Seeing is an illusion. We "see" the world upside-down just as a camera does: the image on your retina is upside-down, but from there on your brain takes over and turns the image right over. As a baby you learned which way up things really are.

Upside-down or inversion illusions are among the most surprising and beautiful perceptual and optical illusions. They reveal how the brain makes sense of the world and give us an indication of its limitations.

Many unexpected phenomena appear when we look at things upside-down. So accustomed are we to vertical symmetry, so unaccustomed to seeing things upside-down, that it is extremely difficult to imagine what most scenes, pictures or objects would look like inverted. Our lifelong conditioning in the way we see things is responsible for a variety of startling upside-down illusions.

In some ways we see things more clearly when we look at them upside-down. For example, landscape artists have been known to check the colors of a scene by the undignified technique of bending over and viewing the landscape through their legs. Its upside-down contours are so unfamiliar that colors can be seen uncontaminated by association with familiar shapes.

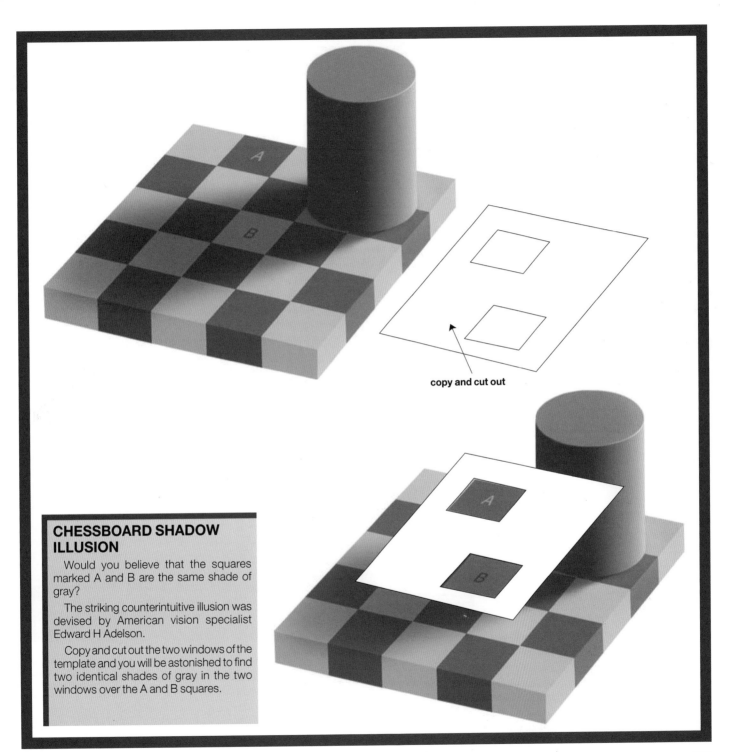

copy and cut out

CHESSBOARD SHADOW ILLUSION

Would you believe that the squares marked A and B are the same shade of gray?

The striking counterintuitive illusion was devised by American vision specialist Edward H Adelson.

Copy and cut out the two windows of the template and you will be astonished to find two identical shades of gray in the two windows over the A and B squares.

PAVEMENT ART

English artist Julian Beever has been creating magnificent trompe l'oeil pavement art using perspective and anamorphism to produce astonishing 3D optical illusions and effects.

PERSPECTIVE STAIRCASE

Apparently random lines become an ordered logical structure when viewed from a specific point in space according to the rules of perspective. The lines painted on the floor and wall looks like a three-dimensional staircase with people standing on it as photographed.

NECKER CUBE

Reality is Perception

The Necker Cube is an optical illusion first published in 1832 by Swiss crystallographer Louis Albert Necker (1786-1861). It is one of the earliest scientific demonstrations of perceptual ambiguity – it is beautiful and fascinating both in its simplicity and for the astonishing phenomenon it produces when we look at it for a while.

The Necker Cube is a line drawing of a wire-frame cube in isometric perspective as shown. It is a two-dimensional skeleton of a three-dimensional cube in which the front cannot be distinguished from the back.

The Necker Cube and many other later ambiguous figures demonstrate that we can "see" something in two (or more) different ways, although what we're looking at remains unchanged.

Looking at a Necker Cube we can't tell the front from the back. Back or front is dependent on what you think it is. The reversal is clearly not in the drawing, it is in you. Your subjectivity accommodates the object first one way, then another. But strangely enough the reversal implies your position in space. When you see the orientation in which the red panel is horizontal the whole cube is below your eyes, you are looking down on it. But when you look at the reversal in which the red panel is vertical, the cube is above your eyes.

Since you can't be in two places at the same time, it is impossible for you to see both orientations simultaneously in the Necker Cube. Thus the perceptual structure of the Necker Cube is far more complex and ambiguous than initially suggested. We never see both orientations together because our visual system must decide where are we positioned in space.

The same reasoning can be applied to drawings of so-called "impossible figures" created by Dutch graphic artist GM Escher (1898-1972), Richard Gregory, Roger Penrose, and others.

Necker was among the first to recognize that both our eyes and brain are involved in the interpretations of images. His discovery of the Necker Cube and its phenomena laid the groundwork for the scientific study of human perception in the 20th century.

AMBIGUOUS NECKER CUBE

As you look at the cube, it suddenly reverses: what had been the front becomes the back, and vice versa. The Necker Cube shows that anything we see is just a "best guess" by our visual system.

The red panels make the Necker Cube less ambiguous and you can see each reversal and orientation clearly.

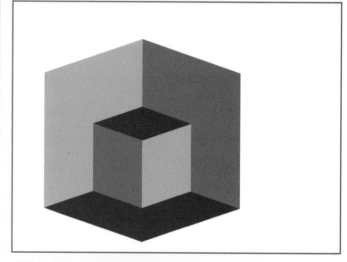

CORNER CUBE

How many different pictures can you see? A small cube in front of a corner of the big cube? A small cube inside a corner of the big cube? Or a small cube cut out and missing from the big cube? If you look for long enough, eventually until all three possibilities will appear before your eyes.

NECKER CUBE LADYBIRD

In how many different locations can you see the ladybird?

NECKER BOX

As you look at the wire skeleton of the Necker Box, missing the clues about its walls, it can reverse into any of the boxes shown at right.

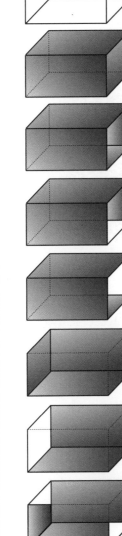

SUBJECTIVE NECKER CUBE

The Necker Cube and its reversals can occur even when it appears as an optical illusion in the form of its subjective contours, as demonstrated.

SUBJECTIVE CONTOURS

We are used to seeing figures defined by specific contours. But sometimes contours can be apparent when in fact no contours are there. For example (right), the Necker Cube is illustrated here by eight red circles in which the corners of the cube appear in white. In spite of the fact that there is no Necker Cube, the illusion of seeing one – complete with its orientation reversals – is surprisingly strong.

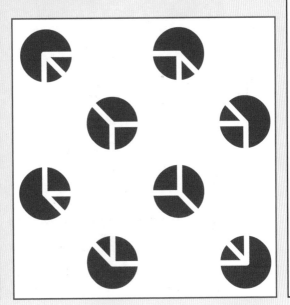

RANDOM-DOT STEREOGRAMS

When we perceive depth and distance we rely on stereoscopic vision, the image perceived by our brain of the two subtly different views received by our two eyes.

Random-dot stereograms were invented by Hungarian Bela Julesz (1928–2003) in the 1960s. He created dual image random-dot stereograms. The procedure he used is presented visually below.

In 1979, Christopher Tyler, a student of Professor Julesz, made a significant improvement to produce the offset scheme that could be applied to create single-image random-dot stereograms, as shown at bottom.

A rectangle of randomly arranged dots

Within the rectangle a group of dots is selected to form a circle

An identical rectangle in which the group of dots forming the circle is shifted a little to the left

When the two rectangles are viewed together as a classical stereo pair, the image of the circle appears to float above the background

A SINGLE-IMAGE RANDOM-DOT STEREOGRAM

The single image technique is a bit more subtle but the basic technique is exactly the same. The single image is divided into a number of narrow columns of random dots. The first column is purely random. The second column is exactly as the first, except that pixels of selected area are shifted a bit to one side. The process is repeated for the whole image to be completed. Columns one and two, columns two and three form a pair, and so on. When you view the picture as explained on the next page you will see a floating circle above the background.

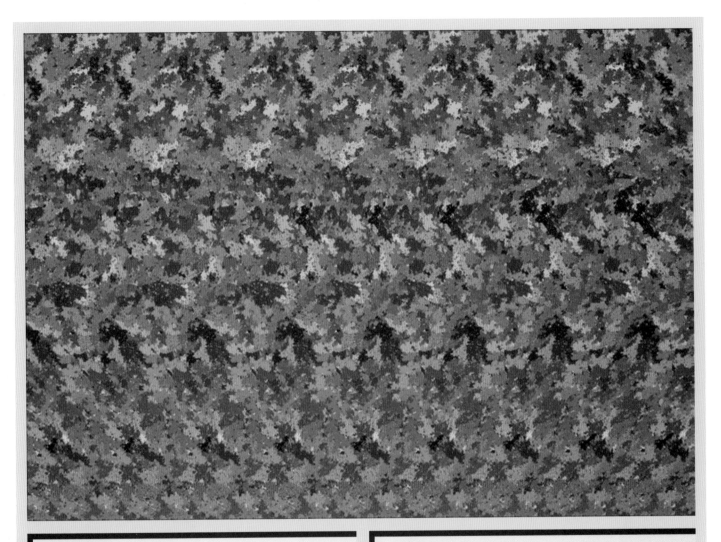

MAGIC EYE

Random-dot Stereograms

In 1991 programmer Tom Baccei and artist Cheri Smith collaborated to improve on the research of Julesz and Tyler. With the help of programmer Bob Salitsky, the group developed the first full-color stereogram program – no more dots but mysterious color images hiding pictures!

Using this program in combination with state-of-the-art 3D modeling software, they developed a totally new, patented art form.

A sample of it is shown above. Can you view it and see the hidden picture?

How to view the stereogram

Normally, when you look at pictures you focus your eyes on the surface of the paper or the computer monitor. When you view Magic Eye stereograms allow you eyes' lines of sight to move outward in parallel and to meet in the distance at a point well beyond the image. About 10 per cent of viewers are unable to perceive stereograms. (Those who can perceive it, will see in the middle of the image a floating tea kettle above a horizontal floor and vertical wall).

PATTERNS IN MATHEMATICS

The world is made up of colors and motion, feelings and thought. Everything in the universe is a kind of pattern. Mathematics is the study of pure pattern.

Because patterns are everywhere – and are often so exquisitely beautiful – they arouse our curiosity. An interest in patterns is something that starts very early in life. When children demonstrate curiosity about the world and its patterns we call it "play;" when mathematicians do so, we call it "research." These patterns may take many forms – numerical, geometric, kinetic, behavioural, and so on.

As the science of pattern, mathematics affects every aspect of our lives: abstract patterns are the basis of thinking, of communications, of computation, of society, and even of life itself.

When we recognize a pattern we see that there is a systematic relationship between elements in a group, and that this indicates an underlying structure of order. When we seek to identify and express this order we are speaking the "language of mathematics."

Patterns are everywhere and everyone can see them, but in mathematics we see patterns within patterns. Part of the magic of mathematics is the way in which a simple and amusing problem can lead to far-reaching insights.

1 2 3 4 5
6 7 8 9 10
11 12 13 14 15
16 17 18 19 20
21 22 23 24 25
26 27 28 29 30

PAIRING PATTERNS AND MEMORY GAMES

Variously known as "pelmanism" or simply "memory," memory games with playing cards have been played for more than 100 years. A set of cards is laid face down on a surface and two cards are flipped face up on each turn: if they are a pair, the player keeps them, otherwise he or she must turn them back face-down but try to remember where they are so they can be found when needed later in the game. Players continue until all the cards have been cleared as pairs. The player with the largest number of pairs of cards at the end is the winner.

This game stimulates observation, concentration, and memory. You don't have to use playing cards – you can play the game with any set of pairs of decorated cards or tiles. You could create an unusually challenging version of the game, for example, by copying the tiles of the pairing patterns problem and cutting them into two sets of matching tiles.

116 **4**

PAIRING PATTERNS

PAIRING PATTERNS PROBLEM

In this abstract version of the classical memory game, how long will it take you to pair up the 30 tiles on the previous page with their identical copies on this page?

1	2	3	4	5
6	7	8	9	10
11	12	13	14	15
16	17	18	19	20
21	22	23	24	25
26	27	28	29	30

Previous page   This page

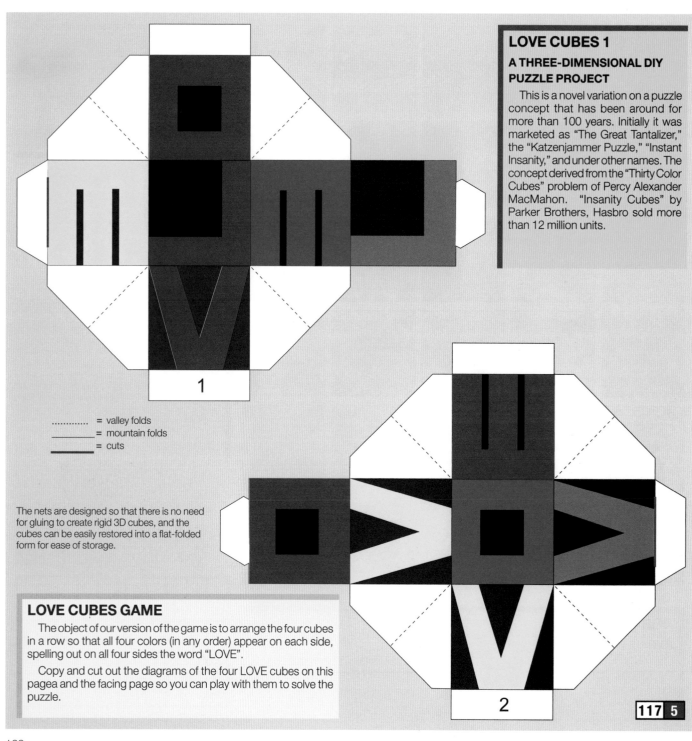

LOVE CUBES 1

A THREE-DIMENSIONAL DIY PUZZLE PROJECT

This is a novel variation on a puzzle concept that has been around for more than 100 years. Initially it was marketed as "The Great Tantalizer," the "Katzenjammer Puzzle," "Instant Insanity," and under other names. The concept derived from the "Thirty Color Cubes" problem of Percy Alexander MacMahon. "Insanity Cubes" by Parker Brothers, Hasbro sold more than 12 million units.

.... = valley folds
───── = mountain folds
▬▬▬ = cuts

The nets are designed so that there is no need for gluing to create rigid 3D cubes, and the cubes can be easily restored into a flat-folded form for ease of storage.

LOVE CUBES GAME

The object of our version of the game is to arrange the four cubes in a row so that all four colors (in any order) appear on each side, spelling out on all four sides the word "LOVE".

Copy and cut out the diagrams of the four LOVE cubes on this pagea and the facing page so you can play with them to solve the puzzle.

117 5

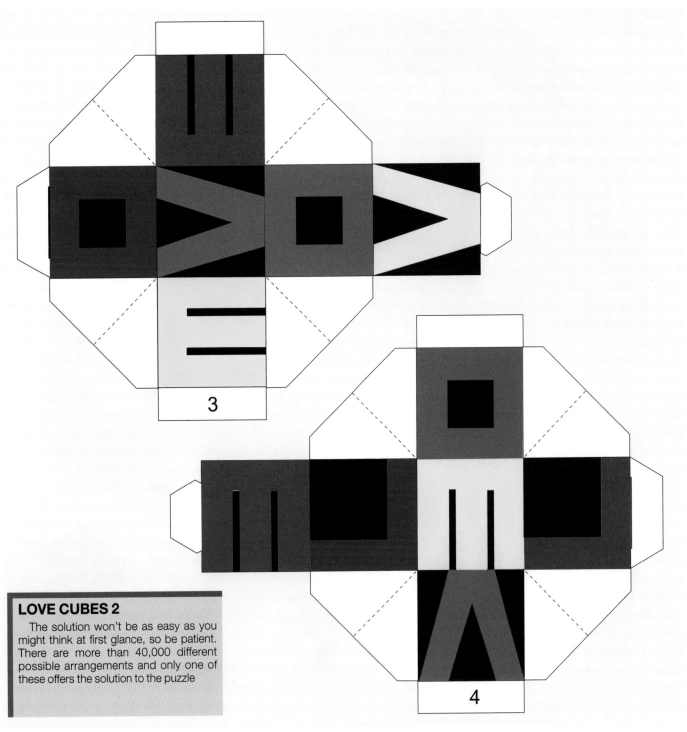

LOVE CUBES 2

The solution won't be as easy as you might think at first glance, so be patient. There are more than 40,000 different possible arrangements and only one of these offers the solution to the puzzle

3

4

163

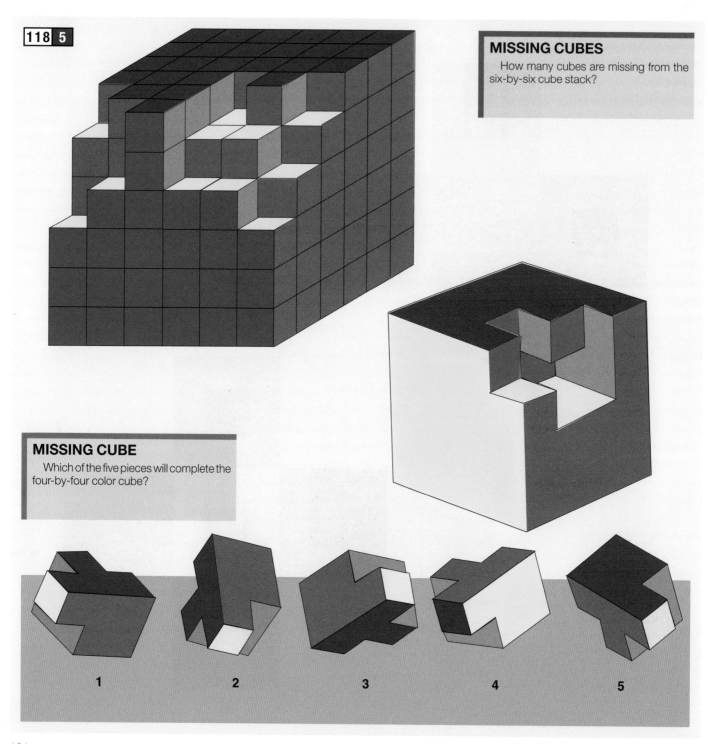

MISSING CUBES

How many cubes are missing from the six-by-six cube stack?

MISSING CUBE

Which of the five pieces will complete the four-by-four color cube?

1   2   3   4   5

164

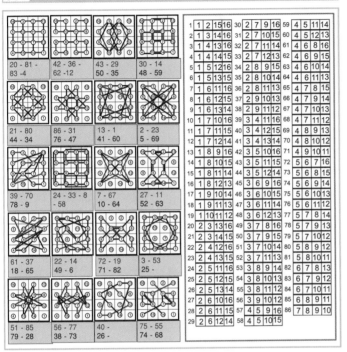

SOLUTIONS

1	2 15 16	30	2 7 9 16	59	4 5 11 14
2	1 3 14 16	31	2 7 10 15	60	4 5 12 13
3	1 4 13 16	32	2 7 11 14	61	4 6 8 16
4	1 4 14 15	33	2 7 12 13	62	4 6 9 15
5	1 5 12 16	34	2 8 9 15	63	4 6 10 14
6	1 5 13 15	35	2 8 10 14	64	4 6 11 13
7	1 6 11 16	36	2 8 11 13	65	4 7 8 15
8	1 6 12 15	37	2 9 10 13	66	4 7 9 14
9	1 6 13 14	38	2 9 11 12	67	4 7 10 13
10	1 7 10 16	39	3 4 11 16	68	4 7 11 12
11	1 7 11 15	40	3 4 12 15	69	4 8 9 13
12	1 7 12 14	41	3 4 13 14	70	4 8 10 12
13	1 8 9 16	42	3 5 10 16	71	4 9 10 11
14	1 8 10 15	43	3 5 11 15	72	5 6 7 16
15	1 8 11 14	44	3 5 12 14	73	5 6 8 15
16	1 8 12 13	45	3 6 9 16	74	5 6 9 14
17	1 9 10 14	46	3 6 10 15	75	5 6 10 13
18	1 9 11 13	47	3 6 11 14	76	5 6 11 12
19	1 10 11 12	48	3 6 12 13	77	5 7 8 14
20	2 3 13 16	49	3 7 8 16	78	5 7 9 13
21	2 3 14 15	50	3 7 9 15	79	5 7 10 12
22	2 4 12 16	51	3 7 10 14	80	5 8 9 12
23	2 4 13 15	52	3 7 11 13	81	5 8 10 11
24	2 5 11 16	53	3 8 9 14	82	6 7 8 13
25	2 5 12 15	54	3 8 10 13	83	6 7 9 12
26	2 5 13 14	55	3 8 11 12	84	6 7 10 11
27	2 6 10 16	56	3 9 10 12	85	6 8 9 11
28	2 6 11 15	57	4 5 9 16	86	7 8 9 10
29	2 6 12 14	58	4 5 10 15		

DÜRER'S DIABOLIC MAGIC SQUARE

There are 880 distinct magic squares of order 4. Dürer's "diabolic" magic square is just one of them. But it contains a surprising number of mathematical patterns.

There are 86 different ways to select four numbers from 1 to 16 to form the magic constant of 34. All of them can be found in Dürer's Diabolic Magic Square as distinct geometrical patterns as shown.

002

MAGIC COLOR (LATIN) SQUARES

Near the end of his life, the great mathematician Leonhard Euler devised a new type of magic square, the Latin square. In a Latin square a number of symbols (numbers, letters, colors, etc.) are placed in a square of the same order so that each row or column contains each symbol only once. For example, a five-by-five square might contain five letters (a, b, c, d, e) five times each in such a way that no two a's appear in the same row or column. There are also diagonal Latin squares, in which the same rules apply also across the two main diagonals or even across all smaller diagonals as well.

The number of Latin squares of order n= 1,2,3 etc. are 1,2, 12, 576, 161280, etc. A further complication is found in the Greco-Latin magic square. This square consists of two Latin squares that have been superimposed so that each cell contains one element of each square, each element of one square is combined with an element of

the second square only once, and each row and column contain every element from both squares. One simple illustration of such a square would be:

1a 2b 3c
2c 3a 1b
3b 1c 2a

It is easy to see that no Greco-Latin magic square of order 2 can exist.

Latin and Greco-Latin magic squares are not mere diversions – they have valuable applications in experimental science. For instance, suppose an agricultural researcher wished to test the effect of seven types of fungicides on wheat plants. He might divide an experimental field into seven parallel strips and treat each strip with a different fungicide. But such a test might be biased because of a favorable field condition in one of the plots – say, in the easternmost or southernmost strip. The best way to control for such biases is to divide the field into 49 plots in a seven-by-seven matrix and apply the chemicals according to the prescriptions of a Latin square. That way each fungicide is tested in every field condition. If the experiment needed to test the seven fungicides on seven different strains of wheat, then a Greco-Latin square could be applied.

In this way Euler's recreational problem has become a widely experimental design, noit only in agriculture but also in biology, sociology, medicine and even marketing. The "cell" need not, of course, be a piece of land. It might be a cow, a patient, a leaf, a cage of animals, a city, a period of time and so on. The square is simply a way to combine variable elements in unique ways.

MAGIC COLOR SQUARES OF ORDER 3

The 12 Magic Color squares of order 3

MAGIC COLOR SQUARES OF ORDER 4

MAGIC DIAGONALCOLOR SQUARES OF ORDER 5

MAGIC COLOR SQUARE OF ORDER 6

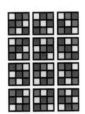

MAGIC COLOR SQUARE OF ORDER7

Note that it is a diagonal magic color square

003
COVER-UP

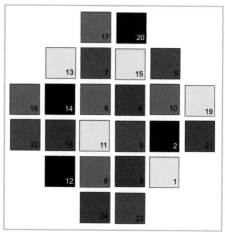

004
MAGIC COLOR SHAPES

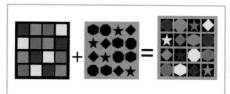

005
THE SPIDER OF JERRY FARRELL

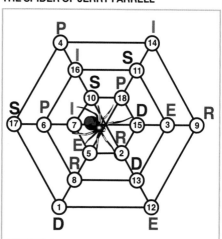

006
DECAPUZ

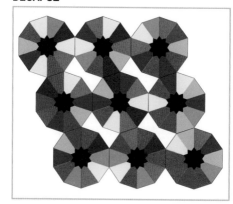

007

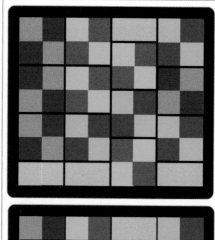

COLOR MATADOR

The solution is believed to be unique, not counting rotations and reflections.

008

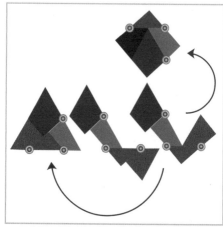

HINGED POLYGONS

The hinged triangle-to-square four pieces transformation of Henry Ernest Dudeney is a real gem of recreational geometry. It has the curious property of folding continuously around the hinges from one position to the other as shown. When you rotate the parts around the red shape counterclockwise you will end up with a square. Rotating the shapes around the red shape clockwise will give an equilateral triangle.

In his book *Canterbury Puzzles* (1907), Dudeney introduced his novel design variation of a four-piece solution for the dissection of a square into an equilateral triangle and vice versa, with the parts hinged together. Thus he created a new puzzle category, that of hinged dissections and tessellations.

009
SAM LOYD'S FOUR-PIECE

010
ARCHIMEDES' STOMACHION

Areas: 144 total.

We do not know whether Archimedes invented the stomachion or merely explored the interesting geometrical properties of an existing dissection puzzle.

The book he wrote about the puzzle was discovered as part of a prayer book from Constantinople (modern Istanbul) in the form of a palimpsest – one or more pages from a scroll or book that has been written on, then scraped off and reused. Dr Reviel Netz, who studied the palimpsest, came to the conclusion that Archimedes was trying to solve the combinatorial problem of finding how many ways there are to form a square from the 14 pieces of the puzzle. The number of solutions he found was 17,152. The stomachion was not only one of the world's oldest puzzles, but also the earliest combinatorial puzzle in the history of mathematics.

Apart from working out the areas of the individual pieces, the object of the game is to rearrange the pieces to form interesting figurative and abstract patterns using all the 14 pieces. One elegant solution – found in a manuscript written by Roman poet and statesman Ausonius (310–395CE) – is in the form of an elephant. American mathematician Bill Cutler has found that there are 536 possible distinct arrangements of the stomachion pieces into a square, where those that are equivalent by rotation and reflection are considered identical.

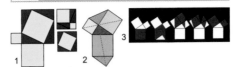

PYTHAGOREAN THEOREM
The Most Beautiful Proofs

(1) Pythagoras's Proof The yellow square in the first diagram is equal to the sum of the two yellow squares in the second diagram, convincingly proving the theorem.

(2) Leonardo's Proof The dotted lines divide Leonardo's diagram into four congruent quadrilaterals.

(3) Baravalle's Proof The fourth step can be explained by Cavalieri's theorem: If a parallelogram is transformed by a shearing transformation without changing its altitude and base, its area does not change.

013

KING'S PLAQUES

By the Pythagorean relationship, the amount of gold in the two smaller plaques is the same as in the big one.

The Pythagorean theorem is well known in the case of square shapes, but it's not widely known that the theorem also holds for any set of geometrically similar figures that can be set together, each on one of the three sides of a right-angled triangle.

The validity of this so-called generalized form of the Pythagorean theorem relates not only to areas but also for the volumes of the figures if their thicknesses are identical.

014

NUMBER LINE

No. There are no whole numbers such that $\sqrt{2} = P/Q$.

The proof is quite simple. Assume $\sqrt{2} = P/Q$, and that P and Q have no common factors. Squaring this equation gives us $P^2 = 2Q^2$, which tells us that P is an even number, of a form $P=2R$. (Here R is any odd or even whole number; you get an even number when you add odd numbers together or when you add even numbers together.) Substituting $P=2R$ into $P^2=2Q^2$ we get $2R^2=2Q^2$, or $R^2=Q^2$, which tells us that Q is also an even number, contrary to our initial assumption that P and Q have no common factors. This contradiction indicates that such natural numbers P and Q don't exist.

The number $\sqrt{2}$ is an irrational number, which mean that it cannot be expressed as a ratio of two whole numbers. It is the number that we multiply by itself to get 2. If we try to write it in decimal form the sequence of digits does not end.

Computers have been used to calculate $\sqrt{2}$ to thousands of digits, but so far no evidence of any pattern or repetition has been found. Numbers in which the sequence of digits does not end are called "nonterminating decimals." Whereas in some, like $\sqrt{2}$, there is no pattern of repetition in the digits, in others – called "repeating decimals" – the sequence can be predicted. For example, 1/3=0.33333333 or 24282/99999= 0.2428124281......

DIAGONAL OF A SQUARE

Simply multiply the length of the square's side by Pythagoras' Constant ($\sqrt{2}$ or 1.4142…).

$6 \times \sqrt{2} = 8.4852$

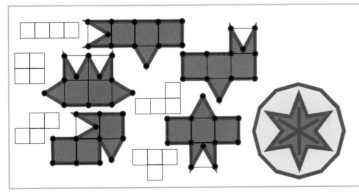

1	2	3	4	5	6	7	8	9	10	11	12	13	14
12	12	24	12	6	12	3	21	6	6	6	3	9	12

011

EGYPTIAN ROPE PUZZLES

(1) There are a large number of polygons with an area of four units that can be made with the Egyptian rope. Elton M Palmer, from Oakmont, Pennsylvania, ingeniously correlated this problem with polyominos, specifically tetrominos. Each of the five tetrominos can be the basis for a large number of solutions, simply by adding and subtracting triangles to accommodate the 12 equal lengths. Some solutions are shown using the five different tetrominos.

(2) Any area from 0 to 11.196 can be encompassed by the Egyptian rope. Eugene J Putzer, Charles Shapiro, and Hugh J. Metz suggested a star configuration solution as shown. By adjusting the width of the star points the largest area is that of a regular dodecagon.

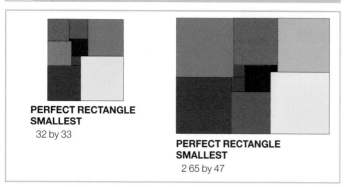

PERFECT RECTANGLE SMALLEST
32 by 33

PERFECT RECTANGLE SMALLEST
2 65 by 47

IMPERFECT SQUARES

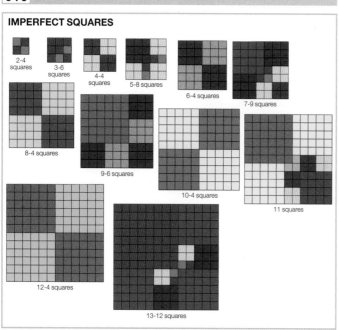

2-4 squares
3-6 squares
4-4 squares
5-8 squares
6-4 squares
7-9 squares
8-4 squares
9-6 squares
10-4 squares
11 squares
12-4 squares
13-12 squares

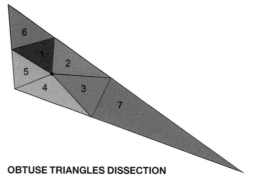

017

OBTUSE TRIANGLES DISSECTION

A beautiful and ingenious proof has been provided by Wallace Manheimer in American *Mathematical Monthly*. The logic of the proof is based on the fact that the obtuse angle must be divided by a line which cannot go to the opposite side, because then it would form another obtuse angle (or two triangles with right angles, which are not acute), which again would have to be dissected, in which case the dissection would not be minimal. This reasoning follows that the line dividing the obtuse angle must end at a point inside the triangle. At this point a minimum of five lines must meet to create vertices of acute angles (less than 90 degrees). This creates an inner pentagon with five triangles. Therefore the minimum number of acute triangles is a total of seven triangles, as shown.

018

EQUILATERAL TRIANGLES DISSECTION
Imperfect Triangles

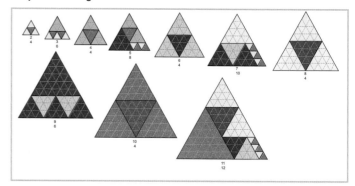

CUBE FOLDS

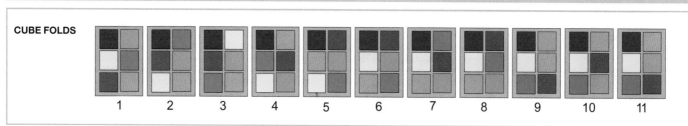

1   2   3   4   5   6   7   8   9   10   11

019

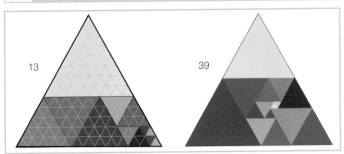

13

39

IMPERFECT TRIANGLE 13

The 13 triangle can be dissected into 12 smaller equilateral triangles

TUTTE'S "PERFECT" EQUILATERAL TRIANGLE

Fifteen triangles – five pairs of identically sized triangles, each pair in a different orientation. If considered different, they form a "perfect" configuration.

EQUILATERAL TRIANGLES DISSECTION

Tutte's "Perfect triangle"

Is a "perfect" tiling of an equilateral triangle possible, i.e. is it possible to dissect an equilateral triangle into the minimal number of smaller equilateral triangle of different sizes (like we did with Perfect Square)?

W.T. Tutte and his colleagues proved that an equilateral triangle cannot be "perfect", and cannot be dissected into equilateral triangles all of different sizes (ignoring orientations). At least two triangles will be of the same size and in the same orientations. However, equilateral triangles can tile in two orientations, in up or down directions. If these are considered as different, since they are not congruent, even if their sizes are identical, then a kind of "perfect" can be found. Tutte found such a "perfect" triangle, the smallest of which is an equilateral with sides of 39 units, all different if orientations of the triangles are considered as different. Thus, it is comparable to Duijvestijn's smallest perfect squares square.

021

PENCIL MAGIC

Although it seems that the pencil just to the left of the top one changes from blue to red, when you remember that all the pencils have moved three places, you can see that in fact it hasn't. It's actually the short blue pencil on the right that has become a short red pencil, just left of the bottom.

023

CUBE HEXOMINOS

2	7	13	14	16	18	21	22	30	33	35

020

DISAPPEARING FACE MAGIC

When you make a cut along the black line as shown, and slide the lower strip one face to the right, a face will seemingly disappear. In fact, scrutiny shows nothing has disappeared. As explained, the secret lies in the fact that there is a progressive increase in the length of the faces from left to the right.

022

PACKING TROMINO CHESSBOARD

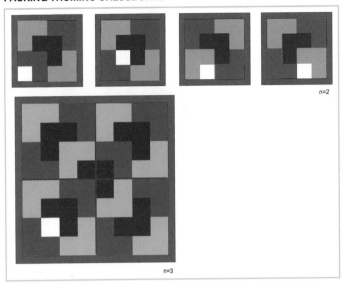

n=2

n=3

025

STEPPING STONES

The Puzzle

By a systematic procedure you can find 32 different configurations.

027

OVERLAPPING TESSELLATIONS

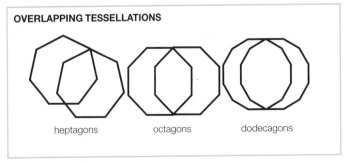

heptagons   octagons   dodecagons

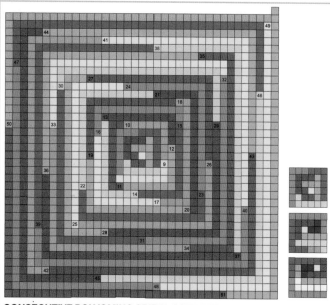

CONSECUTIVE POLYOMINO SPIRAL SQUARES

1. There are many solutions, two are shown.

2. After the smallest square formed by the first eight consecutive polyominos (incorporating the smallest 2-by-3 rectangle), the next rectangle is a 14-by-15 rectangle, formed by the first 20 consecutive polyominos (both shown in white outlines). The area of this rectangle is 210 square units (the 20th triangular number, representing the sum of the first 20 integers).

3. The square is a 35-by-35 square, formed by the first 49 consecutive polyominos. The area of this square is 1,225 square units (the 49th triangular number, representing the sum of the first 49 integers).

4. The formation of a polyomino spiral can continue indefinitely, tesselating the plane; polyominos above 49 (50, 51, etc) have been added to demonstrate this.

FIGURATE TRIANGULAR NUMBERS

Numbers as Patterns

If you wanted to count the dots representing the first 100 consecutive numbers it would be a time-consuming effort.

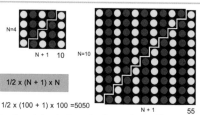

$$1/2 \times (N + 1) \times N$$

$$1/2 \times (100 + 1) \times 100 = 5050$$

Gauss used the ancient method and simple formula shown, to get the result in no time.

028

TESSELLATIONS

There are three regular tessellations. The infinite plane can be covered by equilateral triangles, squares and hexagons without leaving any gaps.

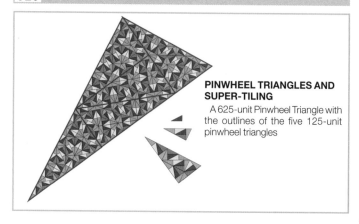

PINWHEEL TRIANGLES AND SUPER-TILING

A 625-unit Pinwheel Triangle with the outlines of the five 125-unit pinwheel triangles

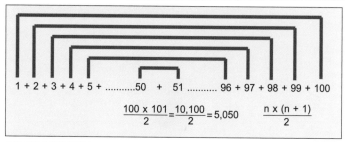

$$\frac{100 \times 101}{2} = \frac{10,100}{2} = 5,050 \qquad \frac{n \times (n + 1)}{2}$$

GAUSS COUNTING

It took Gauss just a few seconds to discover the pattern and conceptualize that there are 50 sums of 101 in the sequence of addition, which gives a total of 5,050. He did not need a calculator or a piece of paper to come to this result. Gauss's feat works for any number "n," not just for 100, according to the general pattern:

$$1+2+3+\ldots + n = n(n+1)/2$$

It is interesting to note that this general formula is also the formula for triangular numbers.

This problem is a beautiful example of the importance of understanding what the problem is really about, in order to find an alternative – a better way of solving the problem than the boring routine of adding the numbers.

Babylonian cuneiform tablets show that the formula for deriving triangular numbers has been known since antiquity. For any number "n," its triangular number (or the sum of the first "n" integers) can be calculated as n(n+1)/2, which is exactly the formula that Gauss used for n = 100.

THE COMBINATORIAL POWER OF TETRAKTYS

There are 10! ways of placing 10 objects. However the triangle looks the same when rotated in any of three different positions, and likewise when flipped over. Therefore, the number of different ways in which the numbers of the Tetraktys can be arranged is (10!)/(2 x 3), which equals 604,800 ways. Note that the '!' needs to be included in the formula becausee 10! means 10 factorial, i.e. 10x9x8x7x6x5x4x3x2x1 = 3,628,800

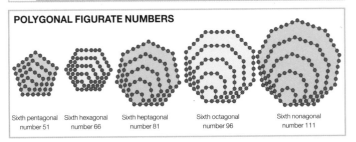

POLYGONAL FIGURATE NUMBERS

Sixth pentagonal number 51 | Sixth hexagonal number 66 | Sixth heptagonal number 81 | Sixth octagonal number 96 | Sixth nonagonal number 111

CONSECUTIVE INTEGERS

We know that triangular figurate numbers are equal to the sum of "n" natural numbers (1, 2, 3, 4, 5, 6 …). Those which are not possible are powers of 2.

1 =	22 = 4 + 5 + 6 + 7
2 = not possible	23 = 11 + 12
3 = 1 + 2	24 = 7 + 8 + 9
4 = not possible	25 = 12 + 13
5 = 2 + 3	26 = 5 + 6 + 7 = 8
6 = 1 + 2 + 3	27 = 8 + 9 + 10
7 = 3 + 4	28 = 1 + 2 + 3 + 4 + 5 + 6 + 7
8 = not possible	29 = 14 + 15
9 = 4 + 5	30 = 4 + 5 = 6 + 7 + 8
10 = 1 + 2 + 3 = 4	31 = 15 + 16
11 = 5 + 6	32 = not possible
12 = 3 + 4 + 5	33 = 10 + 11 + 12
13 = 6 + 7	34 = 7 + 8 + 9
14 = 2 + 3 + 4 + 5	35 = 17 + 18
15 = 4 + 5 + 6	36 = 1 + 2 + 3 + 4 + 5 + 6 + 7 + 8
16 = not possible	37 = 18 + 19
17 = 8 + 9	38 = 8 + 9 + 10 + 11
18 = 5 + 6 + 7	39 = 19 + 20
19 = 9 + 10	40 = 6 + 7 + 8 + 9 + 10
20 = 2 + 3 + 4 + 5 + 6	41 = 20 + 21
21 = 1 + 2 + 3 + 4 + 5 + 6	

035

UNIQUE NUMBERS

Each category (three-digit numbers, four-digit numbers and so on) has a single unique number – that is, the unique number is the same for all three-digit numbers, and a different unique number is the same for all four-digit numbers. You have to make just five calculations to get the answers to my question.

123	198
234	198
345	198
456	198
567	198
678	198
789	198

three digit

1234	3087
2345	3087
3456	3087
4567	3087
5678	3087
6789	3087

four digit

12345	41976
23456	41976
34567	41976
45678	41976
56789	41976

five digit

123456	530865
234567	530865
345678	530865
456789	530865

six digit

1234567	6419754
2345678	6419754
3456789	6419754

seven digit

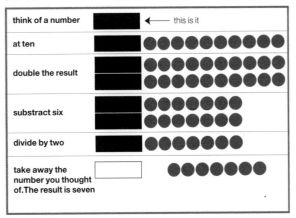

think of a number		← this is it
at ten		
double the result		
substract six		
divide by two		
take away the number you thought of.The result is seven		

THINK OF A NUMBER

Ancient Egyptian mathematicians knew about fixed unknown numbers, calling them "heeps." We shall borrow this idea, and instead of specifying the value of our number we shall consider it as a "heep" (black box). By following the instructions, the secret of the trick will reveal itself in all its simplicity.

1. By working with a number without knowing its value you have just accomplished two things: that is algebra, in which our "heep" would be denoted by a variable, such as "x."

2. Instead of checking specific numbers to see if they worked, you found the problem in general mathematical interpretation, which shows that the trick must always work.

Here's how It work mathematically:

$$\frac{2(x+10)-6}{2} - x$$

$$= \frac{2x + 20 - 6}{2} - x$$

$$= \frac{2x + 14}{2} - x$$

$$= x + 7 - x = 7]$$

There are many instances in algebra and mathematics in general in which complicated proofs can be visualized with geometric diagrams, conveying the proof of a theorem at a glance.

037

THINK OF A NUMBER – AGAIN!

Did you think about a kangaroo eating an orange in Denmark?

Country = Denmark / Last letter = K / Animal = Kangaroo / Last letter = O

Fruit = Orange

TELEPATHIC NUMBER MAGIC

No matter which two-digit number you choose, the answer will always be a multiple of 9, which – you will note – are always the blue numbers. Why is this? Suppose you choose a number of the form 10A+B, where A is the tens digit and B is the units. We are told to subtract the sum of the digits, which is A + B. Hence (10A + B) – A – B = 9A, meaning that we always end up with a multiple of 9.

If you choose 21, (10x2 +1=21) – 2 –1 = 9x2 = 18. If you choose 49, (10x4+9=49) – 4-9 = 36. Both 18 and 36 are multiples of 9.

LOVELY NUMBER 1089

Why is it always 1089?

You will need a little bit of algebra – but stick with it, it is not difficult!

Represent the number with ABC. Reverse this to get CBA. Remember that A is hundreds, B is tens, and C is units.

Take CBA from ABC like this

Hundreds	Tens	Units
A	B	C
C	B	A

Now here is the trick: subtract 1 Hundred, and add 9 Tens and 10 Ones (-100, +90, +10 = 0, so won't change answer):

Hundreds	Tens	Units
A-1	B+9	10+C
-		
C	B	A
=		
A-1-C	9	10+C-A

Last Step: Reverse the answer and add the two numbers together.

A-1-C	9	10+C-A
+		
10+C-A	9	A-1-C
=		
9	18	9

This is 9 hundreds, 18 tens and 9 units, equivalent to 10 hundreds, 8 tens and nine units = 1089.

As predicted, the answer was 1089.

EARRINGS

Nine hundred earrings were worn at the ball. Suppose each of the women wearing two earrings gave one earring to one of the women wearing no earrings. Then everyone would be wearing one earring, so there must be 900 earrings at the party.

ALL FIVES PARADOX

Of the first 1,000 numbers 271 have a 5 in them, which is about 27 per cent.

Surprisingly enough, 99 per cent of the numbers included in the course of counting to our large number (10^{64}), have a 5 in them. This may lead us to think that almost all numbers have a 5 in them.

But there is nothing special about 5. For every number containing a 5, there is a corresponding number with an 8 in the same position (or 9,7,6,4,3,2,1). So almost all very big numbers contain every digit!

All this sounds quite counterintuitive, contrary to what common sense would suggest, and diagrams like ours help in overcoming our initial disbelief.

042

KAPREKAR'S DIGITADITION

Subtract the first number (generator) from the last in the digtaddition series and add the sum of the digits in the last number.

In our example, subtract the first number 23 from the last 115 and add the sum of the digits in the last number (1+1+5=7)

```
 115
 -23
  92
 + 7
  99
```

99 is the sum of all the digits in the partial digitaddition series.

23 +28, 38, 49, 62, 70, 77, 91, 101, 103, 107, 115

5 +10 + 11 + 13 + 8 + 7 + 14 + 10 + 2 + 4 + 8 + 7 = 99

Seeing the secret of this astonishing relationship, Kaprekar exclaimed, "Is this not a wonderful discovery?"

043

KAPREKAR'S MAGIC CONSTANT

Look at the results of the calculations (right). My prediction for all the numbers was 6174. Astonishingly beautiful, isn't it?

Performing this process is called the "Kaprekar routine" or "reverse subtraction process." If you do the routine with any four-digit number, you will always reach 6174. This is "Kaprekar's constant" for all four-digit numbers; it never takes more than seven steps in the series to reach the constant.

There are "Kaprekar's constants" for two-digit and three-digit numbers, also. For two-digit numbers the constants are 9, 81, 63, 27, and 45, forming a cyclic group. For three-digit numbers the constant is 495.

1746	**7652**	**1426**
7641	7652	6421
-1467	-2567	-1246
6174	5085	5175
2435	8550	7551
	-0558	-1557
5432	7992	5994
-2345		
3087	9972	9954
	-2799	-4599
8730	7173	5355
-0378		
8352	7731	5553
	-1377	-3555
8532	6354	1998
-2358		
6174	6543	9981
	-3456	-1899
5644	3087	8082
	8730	8820
6544	-0378	-0288
-4456	8352	8532
2088		
	8532	8532
8820	-2358	-2358
-0288	6174	6174
8532		
8532		
-2358		
6174		

044

COLLATZ PROBLEM OR THE HAILSTONE NUMBERS

Starting with 7, the sequence rises up to 52 before crashing to the endless loop of 1, 4, 2…

7-22-11-34-17-52-26-13-40-20-10-5-16-8-4-2-1-4-2-

None of the numbers from 1 to 26 survive long, but 27 takes us on a long ride. It goes up to 9,232 until at the 77th step the crash starts and finally at the 111th step the 1,4,2… loop is reached.

Physicist Malcolm E Lines in his book *Think of a Number* mentions that all numbers up to one trillion (1,000,000,000,000) have been tested by the University of Tokyo, and every one of these collapses to the 1, 4, 2… loop.

045

NUMBER PALINDROMES

I must apologise if I caused you to undertake a long and arduous effort to produce a palindrome from 89! Martin Gardner noted that of the first 10,000 numbers only 251 do not produce a palindromic number in fewer than 23 steps. Mathematicians conjectured that all numbers would eventually produce a palindrome, but this conjecture has been proven false.

In 1984 Fred Gruenberger showed that among the first 100,000 numbers, 5,996 numbers never generate a palindrome, the first of them being 196.

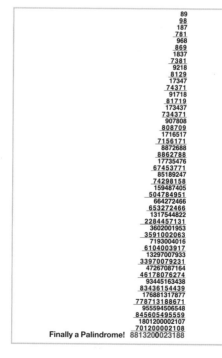

```
                  89
                  98
                 187
                 781
                 968
                 869
                1837
                7381
                9218
                8129
               17347
               74371
               91718
               81719
              173437
              734371
              907808
              808709
             1716517
             7156171
             8872688
             8862788
            17735476
            67453771
            85189247
            74298158
           159487405
           504784951
           664272466
           653272466
          1317544822
          2284457521
          3602001953
          3591002063
          7193004016
          6104003917
         13297007933
         33970079231
        472670087164
        46178076274
        93445163438
        83436154439
       176881317877
       778713188671
       955594506548
       845605495559
      1801200002107
       701200002108
Finally a Palindrome! 8813200023188
```

046

GENERAL'S ARRAY 1

The number of soldiers plus the General must be a square number. The smallest number of soldiers in each group must be 9 in order to create the first square number required for a 10-by-10 square array of soldiers, as shown (right).

GENERAL'S ARRAY 2

The correct arrangement is as illustrated.

047

HOTEL INFINITY

In this case the hotel manager moves everyone to the room whose number is double that of their original room. An infinite number of rooms will be vacated to accommodate the infinite number of arriving guests.

049

CELLULAR PATHS

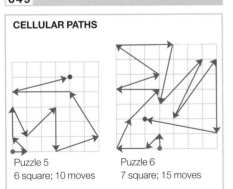

Puzzle 5
6 square; 10 moves

Puzzle 6
7 square; 15 moves

048

6 generations

8 generations

19 generations

CELLULAR AUTOMATON "INFECTED" CHESSBOARD

The board is covered in 17 generations of infected squares. Can you find an initial pattern that will require a larger number of generations before the board is covered?

For each chessboard of n unit sides, the initial number of black squares must be at least n squares for the board to be fully covered. A rectangular square board a x b, needs at least (a + b)/2 infected squares to infect the entire board.

050

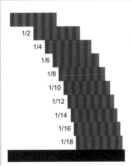

INFINITE OFFSET PARADOX

The surprising answer to this problem is that the offset can be as large as you wish, which sounds quite unbelievable. When you move the top block over the rest so that it just balances, its center of gravity rests over the edge of the block below. Each time you move a block over, you are finding the center of gravity of a new stack of blocks – the block you move plus the blocks above it. The edge of each block acts as a fulcrum supporting all the blocks above it.

If you consider the positions of the centers of gravity of the blocks as the stack is built, it can be seen that the first block will be moved half a block's length along the second block, the top two blocks will be moved one-quarter of a block's length along the third block, the top three blocks will be moved one-sixth of a block's length along the fourth block, and so on.

With an infinite supply of cards or blocks, the offset is the limit of the following number sequence as shown in our stack of 10 blocks:

1/2 + 1/4 + 1/6 + 1/8 + 1/10 + 1/12 + 1/14 + 1/16 + 1/18........

This is called the Harmonic Number Series. The series diverges very slowly, and it would take a great number of blocks to achieve even a small offset. For example, with a deck of 52 cards the maximum overhang if about 2.25 cards' length.

053

THE PATTERN OF THE PRIMES

Instead of trying to predict the exact location of the next prime, Gauss tried to see whether he could at least predict how many prime numbers there were in the first 10, 100, 200, 300, and so on.

When Gauss looked at the proportions of numbers that were primes, counting higher and higher, he saw a pattern emerging. Despite the randomness of the prime numbers, a regularity became obvious. For example, in numbers up to 100, you need to count on average 4 to get from one prime to the next. For N greater than 10,000, every time multiplied by 10, the last column seems to be just increasing on average about 2.3 each time.

The next prime is 1009, at a distance of 11 numbers, which distance should be colored violet.

051

MYSTERY CUBE WALK

The woodworm ate through 41.8 per cent of the volume of the cube, making 418 moves. Can you find a better solution?

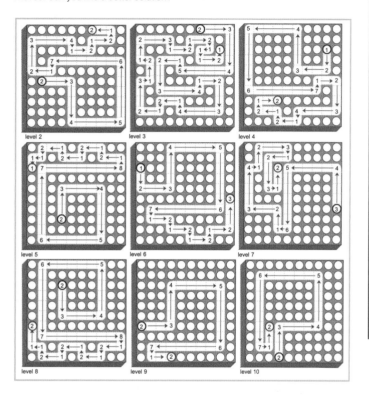

level 2 level 3 level 4
level 5 level 6 level 7
level 8 level 9 level 10

PRIME NUMBERS

Distribution of prime numbers up to 1000

100	2-3-5-7-11-13-17-19-23-29-31-37-41-43-47-53-59-61-67-71-73-79-83-89-97-	**25 primes**
200	101-103-107-109-113-127-131-137-139-149-151-157-163-167-173-179-181-191-193-197-199	**21 primes**
300	211-223-227-229-233-239-241-251-257-263-269-271-277-281-283-293-	**16 primes**
400	307-311-313-317-331-337-347-349-353-359-367-373-379-383-389-397-	**16 primes**
500	401-409-419-421-431-433-439-443-449-457-461-463-467-479-487-491-499-	**17 primes**
600	503-509-521-523-541-547-557-563-569-571-577-587-593-599-	**14 primes**
700	601-607-613-617-619-631-641-643-647-653-659-661-673-677-683-691-	**16 primes**
800	701-709-719-727-733-739-743-751-757-761-769-773-787-797-	**14 primes**
900	809-811-821-823-827-829-839-853-857-859-863-877-881-883-887-	**15 primes**
1000	907-911-919-929-937-941-947-953-967-971-977-983-991-997-	**14 primes**
LIST OF PRIME NUMBERS LESS THAN 1000	**A total of**	**168 primes**

PRIME NUMBERS STAIRCASE

According to Goldbach's Conjecture, every even number bigger than 2 is the sum of two primes. In our staircase of primes we can create all the even numbers up to 446.

PRIME SPIRAL

213	212	211	210	209	208	207	206	205	204	203	202	201	200	199
214	161	160	159	158	157	156	155	154	153	152	151	150	149	198
215	162	117	116	115	114	113	112	111	110	109	108	107	148	197
216	163	118	81	80	79	78	77	76	75	74	73	106	147	196
217	164	119	82	53	52	51	50	49	48	47	72	105	146	195
218	165	120	83	54	33	32	31	30	29	46	71	104	145	194
219	166	121	84	55	34	21	20	19	28	45	70	103	144	193
220	167	122	85	56	35	22	17	18	27	44	69	102	143	192
221	168	123	86	57	36	23	24	25	26	43	68	101	142	191
222	169	124	87	58	37	38	39	40	41	42	67	100	141	190
223	170	125	88	59	60	61	62	63	64	65	66	99	140	189
224	171	126	89	90	91	92	93	94	95	96	97	98	139	188
225	172	127	128	129	130	131	132	133	134	135	136	137	138	187
226	173	174	175	176	177	178	179	180	181	182	183	184	185	186
227	228	229	230	231	232	233	234	235	236	237	238	239	240	241

BINARY ABACUS

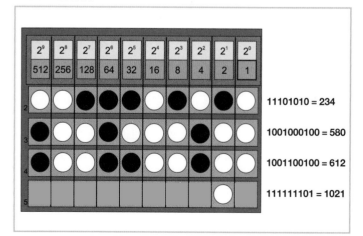

2^9	2^8	2^7	2^6	2^5	2^4	2^3	2^2	2^1	2^0
512	256	128	64	32	16	8	4	2	1

11101010 = 234
1001000100 = 580
1001100100 = 612
111111101 = 1021

TOWER OF HANOI

Lucas' famous puzzle was manufactured as a children's toy. It is an ingenious model for the concept of geometric exponential series. Even today, a version of the puzzle can be found in toy stores worldwide.

Only seven moves are needed for the transfer of the three coins.

For transferring 4 coins 15 moves will be necessary, for 5 coins 31, and for 6 coins 63.

In general for transferring "n" coins, $2^n - 1$ moves will be necessary.

The solution to Babylon can be quite elusive because it is so easy to make a mistaken move.

Here's a hint towards the solution:

1- Move the smallest disk from its present column to the next, always in the same cyclic order and

2- Thereafter, move any disk except the smallest. This rule seems arbitrary, but you will find there is always one legal move you can make within it--until the puzzle is suddenly and miraculously solved (not necessarily in the fewest number of moves).

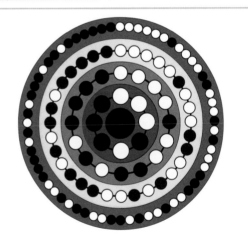

058

BINARY MEMORY WHEEL
Four wheels:

Red: 3-bit binary numbers.

This is a unique solution. Longer binary wheels are used to code messages in telephone transmission and radar mapping. University of California mathematician Sherman K Stein called such binary structures "memory wheels;" they were also known as "Ouroborean wheels" after the mythological snake (the Ouroboros) that ate its own tail.

Green: 4-bit binary numbers. One solution shown.

Yellow: 5-bit binary numbers.

Blue: 6-bit binary numbers.

059

ZENO'S PARADOXES
Achilles and the Tortoise

The fault in Zeno's argument is the assumption that the sum of an infinite number of numbers is always infinite.

The infinite sum of

1 + 1/2 + 1/4 + 1/8 + 1/16 + 1/32 + 1/64 ... equals 2.

This is known as a *geometric series*. (A *geometric series* is a sequence that begins with 1 and in which the successive terms are those multiplying the previous term by a fixed amount, say 'x', which in this case is 1/2. Infinite geometric series are converging to a finite number when 'x' is less than one.)

The distance that Achilles travels and the time it takes him to reach the tortoise can both be expressed as infinite geometric series in which x is less than one and so the total distance Achilles traverses to catch up with the tortoise is not infinite. The same goes for the time required.

Suppose Achilles gave a 10 meter head start to the tortoise, and he runs at 1 meter per second, ten times faster than the tortoise. It takes Achilles 5 seconds to cover half this distance. Half the remaining distance will take him 2.5 seconds, and so on, covering the total distance in a finite 10 seconds according to the mentioned infinite geometric series. By that time the tortoise has moved to the point of 11 meters. We know that Achilles should pass the tortoise at a point of 11.11 meters from the points Achilles started, taking him 11 seconds to reach that point, and so winning the race.

The usefulness of Zeno's paradoxes is that they gave birth to the idea of convergent infinite series, crystallizing a number of mathematical concepts. The main one among these was the notion of *limits*. Interest in paradoxes was strongly revived during the Renaissance, when more than 500 collections of paradoxes are known to have been published.

060

TRUTH CITY ROAD

Ask the man, "Please point to the road leading to the city you are from?" If the man is from Truth City, he will point to its road. If he is from the City of Liars, he will also point in the same direction. The interesting thing about his answer is that, although you have obtained the directions you asked for, you don't really know whether the man told you the truth or lied.

TRUTH AND MARRIAGE

The young man should ask one of the daughters: "Are you married?" Regardless of which daughter is asked the question, a "Yes" answer means Amelia must be married, while a "No" means Leila must be married. If Amelia is asked the question, her answer must be the truth – if it is "Yes", she is married and if it is "No", she is not married, so Leila must be. On the other hand, if the question is asked of Leila, her answer must be a lie – if it is "Yes" she is not married, and Amelia must be, if it is "No" it is a lie, so she is married.

TRUTH, LIES AND INBETWEEN

Ask the man this question twice: 'Are you one of those who alternately lie and tell the truth?' If he answers "No" twice, he must be a truth-teller. If he answers "Yes" twice, he must be a liar. If he answers "Yes" and then "No", he must be a member of the group who alternately lie and then tell the truth.

CAKES, JELLY AND PUDDING

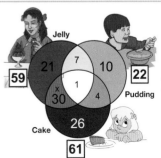

The Venn diagram plots the information about the party very clearly.

There are 99 children at the party. 59 eat jelly; 22 eat pudding; 61 eat cake. 1 eats jelly, pudding and cake; 7 eat jelly and pudding; 4 eat pudding and cake.

57 eat only one item. These are 21 who only eat jelly, plus 26 who only eat cake, and 10 who only eat pudding. There is nobody who doesn't eat anything at all.

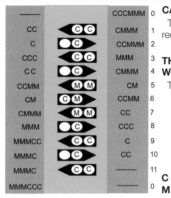

CANNIBALS AND MISSIONARIES

There are four different solutions all requiring 11 moves, one of them shown.

THREE HUSBANDS AND THREE WIVES

This also requires 11 crossings.

C = cannibals
M = missionaries

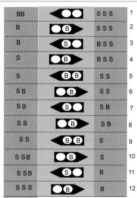

063

RIVER-CROSSING SOLDIERS

The five soldiers take 15 crossings to get to the other side of the river. Both boys go to the other side of the river. One of them brings back the boat. A soldier crosses. The boat returns with the other boy. Both boys cross the river, one of them returns with the boat, the second soldier crosses. Four crossings are needed for one soldier, altogether 15 crossings for 5 soldiers. The solution is shown in the diagram.

B = boys
S = soldiers

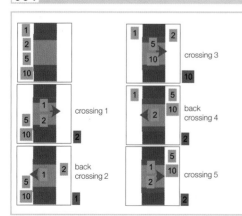

064

NIGHT CROSSING

The four hikers just made it. They crossed in 17 minutes, just before the bridge collapsed. The first solution is shown in the artwork. In the other solution, in move 2 hiker 2 is crossing back.

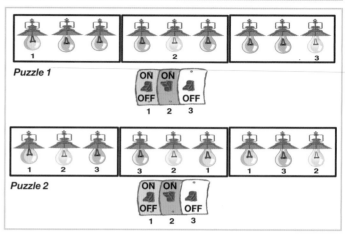

Puzzle 1

Puzzle 2

LAMPS IN THE ATTIC

Many claim that there is not enough information provided to solve this problem. But that is because they have taken too narrow a view. The key is understanding what a lightbulb does: it produces not only light but heat, and it remains warm many minutes after it has been switched off. With that in mind you can find the solution to both problems fairly easily

Puzzle 1

First, turn on switch 1 and leave it on for several minutes so that the bulb will get hot. Next, turn off switch 1 and turn on switch 2, and then go quickly to the attic. If the light is on, then switch 2 works the lamp; if the bulb is dark but warm, switch 1 works the lamp; if the bulb is both dark and cold, switch 3 – the one that has not been used – works the lamp.

Puzzle 2

You do exactly as before. The hot lamp is turned on by switch 1, the burning lamp by switch 2, while the cold lamp must be operated by switch 3 – which has not been used.

LANGFORD'S PROBLEMS

Puzzle 1 - Four teams, two in each team

The first three runners are blue, green, and yellow. This is a unique solution for four pairs of the so-called Langford's Problem, which in general form is: if n is the number of pairs, the problem has a solution only if n is a multiple of 4 or 1 less than such a multiple. The problem was stated by Scottish mathematician C Dudley Langford after watching his son playing with colored blocks.

Puzzle 2 - Nine teams, three in each team

For this puzzle n=9: Langford and colleagues found one unique solution, as shown.

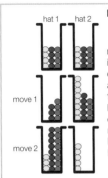

HAT MAGIC

Twelve eggs.

See the illustration. In move 1, the worst scenario is to transfer four eggs of one color plus one of another color. In move 2, the worst scenario would be to transfer 9 + 3 = 12 eggs to satisfy the requirement to have at least 3 eggs of one color in hat 1.

HATS AND COLORS 1

Clown B. If clown A would see two red or two green hats he would know the color of his hat (as well as of that of the hidden clown) and he would shout it aloud. But what he sees is only one of each color, not offering him any clue. Therefore, clown B should come to the conclusion that the color of his hat must be the opposite of the color of the hat he sees before him.

HATS AND COLORS 2

Clown A sees two red hats and one blue hat. His hat can be either red or blue. Clown B knows that A sees only one blue hat. Therefore he can deduce that the color of his own hat must be red. Clown C can't know the color of his hat.

But the question asked you to determine who could deduce the color of clown A's hat. Only clown D can do this. He knows that clown A sees neither two blue hats (or he would know his own hat is red) nor three red hats (or he would know his own hat is blue). Therefore clown D knows that clown A can see two red hats and one blue hat, leaving one red hat and one blue hat to be worn by clowns A and E in some order. Since clown D can see clown E's hat, clown D knows that clown A is wearing the color of hat that clown E is not wearing.

BIRTHDAY PROBLEMS

(1) 23. This problem is a good example of the difficulty in using common sense in judging probability problems. The intuitive guess of most people in answering this question is usually 150 or more. In our question, for only 23 people in a randomly selected group, the odds of two having the same birthday are better than 50-50. This result may be surprising, and may convince you that it is better to depend in this case on the mathematical theory of probability than on intuition.

The reasoning is as follows: With two in a group, the probability of them having different birthdays is high: 364/365. With three it is 364/365 x 363/365: As a group of three still contains a group of two, the fractions are

DRAGON FIGHT

Two possible solutions are illustrated, both requiring nine cuts of the sword. Can you do it in fewer cuts?

multiplied. The probability of having the same birthday increases as the probability of having different birthdays diminishes. When you think about the problem combinatorially, among the 23 people there are really 253 possible pairings, making it more believable that such a small number of people is sufficient.

$(364/365) \times (363/365) \times .... \times (365 - n + 1)/365$

where n is the total number of people.

The total number of pairings among n people:

$n \times (n-1)/2$ which is equal $1+2+3+ ..... + n-1$

For a year of n days and a random collection of r people the probability of at least two people having the same birthday is 1 minus the probability of everybody having different birthdays:

$P_n(r)=1 - (n/n \times n-1/n \times n-2/n \times .... \times n-(r-1))/n = 1 - n!/n^r(n-r)!$

(2) The answer is 253.

The probability of a coincidence is $1 - (364/365)^n$ where n is the number of people besides yourself.

WATERMELON PARADOX

The watermelon weighed 5 kilograms when it arrived at the diner's table. See the demonstration in this diagram.

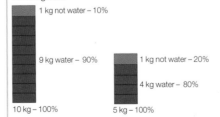

1 kg not water – 10%

9 kg water – 90%

10 kg – 100%

1 kg not water – 20%

4 kg water – 80%

5 kg – 100%

CONSECUTIVE WATERMELONS

The heaviest watermelon weighed 13 kilograms.

?	?	?	7	?	?	?
1	3	5	7	9	11	13

BIG WHEEL OF FORTUNE

Don't bet – it's a sucker's bet. Two spins will land in the same slot 94 per cent of the time. Using the same formula we used in Birthday Problems, the calculation for this probability is:

$1 - (360! / (360^{45} \times 315!)) = 94.3 \%$.

THREE COINS FLIP

This is bad reasoning. We already know that there are two different ways for a single coin to land. We have also seen that there are four different ways for two coins to land. We can show that there are eight different ways for three coins to turn up. Here they are:

HHH HHT HTH HTT THH THT TTH TTT.

We can see that only two of the eight cases show all three coins the same. Therefore, the correct probability is 2/8 = 1/4.

FLIPPING A COIN FIVE TIMES

Each time the coin is tossed there are two possible outcomes. We can conclude from the "basic counting law" that the total number of outcomes is given by

$2 \times 2 \times 2 \times 2 \times 2 = 2^5 = 32$

Basic Counting Law

If there are m possible ways a task can be performed and, after the first task is completed, there are n possible ways for a second task to be performed, then there are m x n possible ways for the two task to be performed in order.

FLIPPING COIN GAME

Although each player has an equal chance of getting a head at each toss, the player who tosses first has a clear advantage no matter how long the game lasts. Let's identify the players as Red and Green. Red will win in the following scenarios:

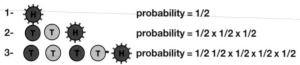

1-   probability = 1/2

2-   probability = 1/2 x 1/2 x 1/2

3-   probability = 1/2 1/2 x 1/2 x 1/2 x 1/2

4- etc. etc. etc.

The overall probability of the first player winning is simply the sum of the probabilities of each of the above scenarios that is:

(1/2) + (1/2 x 1/2 x 1/2) + (1/2 x 1/2 x 1/2 x 1/2 x 1/2) + ...,

which is a series containing an infinite number of terms, which in our case is 2/3.

Since eventually either Red or Green must win, the probability of Green winning is simply 1 minus the probability that Red wins – that is, 1 - 2/3 = 1/3.

As we see, the first player has twice as much chance of winning as the second player, which is a surprising conclusion. The best way to check this outcome is to play the game for a while.

BALANCING COINS

It turns out that the edge of a penny is not perpendicular to its faces. This slight beveling allows the penny to (or other coins as well) to drops easily out of the mold when it is cast.

074

TOSSING A COIN 100 TIMES

The chances of getting 100 heads in 100 tosses of a coin:

1 head: 1/2 = 0.50

2 heads: 1/2 x 1/2 = 1/4 = 0.25

3 heads: 1/2 x 1/2 x 1/2 = 1/8 = 0.125

100 heads = $(1/2)^{100}$ =1/1,000,000,000,000,000,000,000,000,000,000

It is theoretically possible to get 100 heads in 100 tosses of a coin, but it is mind-bogglingly unlikely because there are so many different configurations of mixed heads and tails.

Still, if or the same reason, it is equally unlikely that you will get any other specific sequence. All the sequences shown have equally the same likelihood of occurring.

075

BENFORD'S LAW: THE LONGEST RUN OF HEADS/ TAILS
Test 1 is a fake.

Dr. T. P. Hill explained the coin-tossing experiment in American Scientist magazine, in the July-August 1998 issue. A "quite involved calculation" revealed a surprising probability. The overwhelming odds are that at some point in a series of 200 tosses, either head or tails will come up six or more times in a row. Most fakers do not know this and avoid guessing (and faking) such long runs of heads to tails, which they mistakingly believe to be improbable. At just a glance he could see whether or not a student's 200 coin-tossing results contain a run of six heads or tails; if they don't, the student's result is judged to be a fake.

Benford's Law is a rule obeyed by a stunning variety of phenomena. Even a randomly selected number of figures extracted by newspapers will obey the law's demands that around 30% of the numbers will start with a 1, 18% with a 2, right down to just 4.6% starting with a 9.

This sounds like an unbeliavable paradox. Why so?

A phenomenological law also called the "first digit law", "first digit phenomenon", or "leading digit phenomenon". Benford's law states that in listings, tables of statistics, etc., the digit 1 tends to occur with a much greater probability than the expected 11.1% (i.e., one digit out of 9). Benford's law can be observed, for instance, by examining tables of logarithms and noting that the first pages are much more worn and smudged than later pages (Newcomb 1881). While Benford's law applies to many situations in the real world, a satisfactory explanation has been given only recently through the work of Hill (Hill's theorem, 1996).

What it means is, that while some phenomena are under control of a single distribution such as, for example, the bell curve, many more are dictated by a random mix of all kinds of distributions.

Deviations of Benford's Law can be easily detected using standar statistical tests (digital analysis) and are used today to detect frauds. Nature's preference for certain numbers, such as the Golden ratio or the Fibonacci sequence, has been known for a long time. Benford's law is now regarded as another beautiful and fundamental feature of the mathematical universe.

In a nice little twist, the three are linked. The ratios of successive terms in a Fibonacci sequence tend toward the Golden ratio, while the digits of all the numbers making up the Fibonacci sequence tend to conform to Benford's law!

076

SCATTERHEAD

After six experiments of counting the number of randomly appearing beads shown in the windows of Scatterhead, we get the following result: red = 31; green = 6; yellow = 7; blue = 16. This is quite a good approximation of the true distribution of 60 colored balls hidden in the box.

The true distribution of the colored beads in the box was: red = 30; green = 6; yellow = 9; blue = 15.

Statistics is a science that studies the collection and meaning of data. Statistics uses samples, such as groups of objects or the scores of tests, selected from a large group under consideration. A random sample is one picked out by chance. Thus, probability is a very important topic in statistics. Statistics uses polls by means of which estimates are made on the composition of a large group by determining the opinion of a sample.

Statistics also tells us how much risk we take of being wrong. We reduce the risk by using a big number of samples. If you know something about statistics, you will not be fooled by false statements based on wrong interpretations of data encountered everywhere around us today.

Graphs are very useful and often used in statistics and probability. They provide a visual representation of numerical facts and quickly summarize relationships of data, making it easier to understand and interpret correctly.

077

RANDOM WALK

Probability theory says that after "n" flips, the walker will be, on average, a distance of the square-root of "n" ($\sqrt{n}$) away from the starting point at the middle. For 36 flips this distance would be 6 marks left or right of the middpoint. Despite this, the chance of eventually returning to the start is 100%, although it may take a long time for this to happen. A very interesting question arises here: "How often is the walker likely to change sides?".

The most interesting aspect of the one-dimensional random walk appears if there are no barriers at all. The question then arising is, "How often is the walker likely to change sides?" Because of the walk's symmetry, you might expect that in a long random walk, the walker would spend about half of his time on each side of the starting point. Exactly the opposite is true! The most probable number of changes from one side to the other is 0.

RANDOM DRUNKARD'S WALK

We really cannot say where the drunkard will be at the end of his walk, but we can answer the question about his most probable distance from the lampost after a given number of flips.

The most probable distance D from the lampost after a certain large number of irregular turns is equal to the average length of each straight track of the walk L, multiplied by the square root of their total number N. So the formula is:

$$D = L \times \sqrt{N}$$

The drunkard will eventually get back to the safety of the lampost with certainty on a two-dimensional finite square grid, as in our game.

When there are no barriers and the random walk is not finite the situation becomes quite complex, giving rise to many unsolved problems and theories. The situation is even more complex in a 3-dimensional random walk along a finite space lattice.

The big surprise here is that a random walker is certain to reach any intersection in a finite time. In practical terms, if you are inside a large building or a maze with a very complex network of corridors and passages, you can be sure of reaching an exit in a finite time by walking randomly through the structure.

RANDOMNESS

Science and math differentiate between processes that are **deterministic** and those that are **stochastic**, which means dependent on chance. The word "stochastic" derives from the Greek word for 'target', indicating something random in character.

Preoccupation with randomness has permeated 20th century sicence, and has a close relationship with **Thermodynamics**, in which *entropy* is a measure of disorder. Randomness became the foundation of **Quantum Mechanics**, a chance element in the microstructure of the universe. Eventually, it may turn out that behind this apparent disorder, there are non-random laws yet to be discovered. The influence of these ideas is felt in many other fields too; in the random art of abstract expressionism; in random music, etc.

An enormous amount of research has been done on the so called '**random walk**' problem, which models the diffusion of molecules under random collisions in gases and liquids, and are also excellent tools to analyze games of chance.

078

RANDOM PATTERNS?

In a random pattern, the color of any cell would give us no clue to the color of the next one. This is true of the pattern on the left.

The right-hand pattern *looks* more random to most people. But it is not, because rate of color change is too-high when moving from one cell to the other.

079

TRIPLE DUEL

Amazingly Mike's chances are twice as good as those of Tom and Bill!

Why? Tom and Bill will obviously shoot at each other (as representing the greater threat) and Mike will then have first shot at the survivor--with a 50% chance of hitting him (and so being the overall winner), and a 50% chance of missing (and so being shot himself).

Now comes the interesting part: If Mike has first shot he will aim to miss, for if he kills either Tom or Bill then the other will kill him. So there are really only two cases to consider:

1- Tom shoots first and kills Bill, or vice versa.

2- In each case Mike has a 50% of hitting the survivor, so his overall probability is 1/2.

Tom's chance is 1/2 if he shoots first, but 0 if Bill shoots first, so his overall probability is only 1/2 x 1/2=1/4. B has the same probability.

Many of the results of game theory are counterintuitive and such problems became very popular in recreational mathematics literature, like the "Triple Duel" in its many different variations. It is a beautiful classic puzzle from probability theory with an absolutely counterintuitive conclusion.

080

MOEBIUS BAND CUT ALONG THE MIDDLE

One piece, two edges, double twists, double length.

MOEBIUS BAND CUT NEAR THE EDGE

Two linked bands, one of them a Moebius of the same length, the other a band ot twice the length with two complete twists

TRAVELER'S PATH ALONG A MOEBIUS BAND

The traveler and his watch follow a path that brings them back to their starting point but mirror reversed. The Moebius band is therefore a non-orientable surface. Non-orientability is a unique

property of the Moebius band.

081

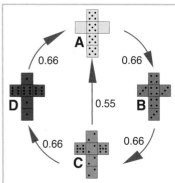

NON-TRANSITIVE DICE

The set of dice convincingly demonstrate the probability paradox that breaks the rules of transitivity. So, the can be said to be non-transitive.

Dice A beats dice B. Dice B beats dice C. Dice C beats dice D, and finally, dice D beats dice A.

The game has a circular winning arrangement, which can be worked out and "proved" by creating score charts listing all encounters between two dice in the set.

082

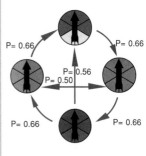

NON-TRANSITIVE SPINNERS

When any two spinners are playing against each other, there are 36 possible outcomes. Taking spinner A and B, therefore, we can see that 24 times out of 36 A will show value 4, therefore beating the value 3 of B (which appear 36 times). With B and C, value 2 of C appears 24 times, allowing B to win. With C and D, the answer is also 24. These results are also shown in diagrammatic form in the score charts below.

Surprisingly enough, the contest between A and D shows that D beats A 24 times out of 36 times too – a non-transitive paradox!

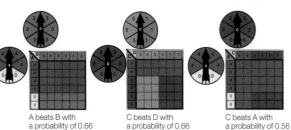

A beats B with a probability of 0.66

C beats D with a probability of 0.66

C beats A with a probability of 0.56

083

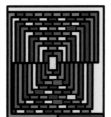

FIFTH COLOR

Look at the date of publication – McGregor's map was, of course, an April Fool's joke! The Four-color problem has been solved, and is now the Four-Color Theorem, which tells us that for any map in the plane four colors are sufficient to color it in such a way that no adjacent regions have the same color.

After the map's publication, Martin Gardner received hundreds of letters with the map colored with four colors; one such solution is shown above.

FOUR COLOR THEOREM

084

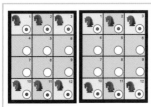

KNIGHTS EXCHANGE

The solution requires 16 moves:
(1) 3–4 (2) 4–9 (3) 11–4 (4) 4–3 (5) 1–6
(6) 6–11 (7) 12–7 (8) 7–6 (9) 6–1
(10) 2–7 (11) 7–12 (12) 9–4 (13) 10–9
(14) 9–2 (15) 4–9 (16) 9–10

085

GOLDEN RINGS NECKLACE

If you cut any of the two rings in the second row from bottom you will be able to separate the necklace into three parts, consisting of 1 – 1 – 9 rings.

The three lowest rings are Borromean rings, three rings joined in such a way that no pair are interlinked but the three cannot be separated. They are so called after the Italian Renaissance family, the Borromeo, who used them on their coat of arms. If you cut any one of the rings, all three will be separated.

It has recently been shown that true Borromean circles are impossible, whatever their relative sizes. However, they can be made from three congruent elliptical rings.

086

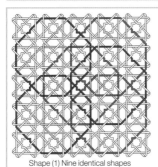

Shape (1) Nine identical shapes

Shape (2) 12 identical shapes in four different orientations

Shape (3) Four identical shapes in four different orientations

087

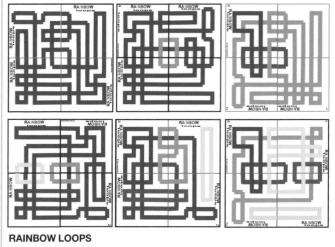

RAINBOW LOOPS

Configurations with 1 to 6 loops

088

Solid	Vertices (V)	Edges (E)	Faces (F)	V - E + F
Tetrahedron	4	6	4	2
Cube	8	12	16	2
Octahedron	6	12	8	2
Icosahedron	12	30	20	2
Dodecahedron	20	30	12	2

REGULAR POLYHEDRA CHART

The insight that V - E + F = 2 is always 2, is called the "Euler characteristic." It is a great insight about any connected doodle that we can make in the plane. The chart also shows that all the regular solids have the same relationship of vertices, edges, and faces expressed in the Euler characteristic.

ALHAMBRA MOSAIC PATTERN

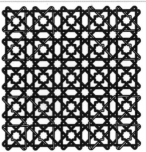

The pattern is composed of 25 interlocking closed loops of three shapes in different orientations as shown.

089

FOLDING THREE STAMPS
You can achieve the complete set of 6 permutations by folding.

FOLDING A STRIP OF FOUR STAMPS
The 16 possible folds are as shown.
The numbers relate to the options
given in the puzzle

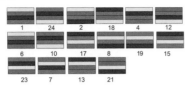

FOLDING EIGHT STAMPS
Fold the right half over the left so that 2 goes on 5, 3 on 6, 1 on 4 and 8 on 7. Now fold the bottom half up so that 4 goes under 5, and 7 under 6. Then tuck 4 and 5 between 6 and 3, and fold 1 and 2 over the stack.

FOLDING NEWS
The Power of Doubling
Surprisingly enough you will be wrong if your answer was more than 10 times, since it is practically impossible to fold the page of a newspaper in half more than 8 or at the very most 10 times, no matter how large or thin is the sheet.

To understand why this should be so is to realize that doubling something is to multiply it by 2, which is the same as adding a number to itself. Yet something so simple can be very powerful. After nine folds tha thickness of the paper is 512 times as thick as it was at the start. This thickness prevents further folding, unless you are one of those muscular giants able to perform such feats. Repeated doubling soon leads to huge numbers.

090

FOLDING SIX STAMPS
Fold 3 is impossible. In general, it is not possible to fold the strip to make the diagonally-appearing colors adjacent in the final stack

FOLDING A SQUARE OF FOUR STAMPS
The eight possible folds are as follows.

091

IMPOSSIBLE ART GARDEN
The sculpture is based on the celebrated "hyper-card" fold, which can be created using a single piece of paper with three cuts, as shown. Fold the yellow up 90 degrees along the broken line and then turn the right portion (white) back by folding it back 180 degrees along half the broken line on its side. Many variations on this design have been created since Martin Gardner revealed it. Robert Neal and other magicians have devised a number of great magic tricks based on the hyper-card.

This model of the "impossible" garden sculpture can be made from one rectangular sheet of paper.

092

HARRY'S IMPOSSIBLE FOLDING PUZZLE
The solution is as shown.

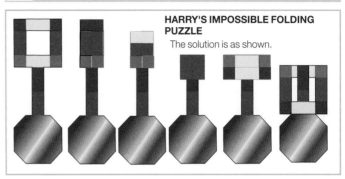

093

IVAN'S "IMPOSSIBLE" FIVE-FOLD LOOP PUZZLE
The "impossible" sculpture was inspired by a topological mechanism discovered by Rolamite Inc. It seems as if the whole structure has passed through each of the five slots – an apparently impossible feat. But as impossible as it looks, you can do it, and in just a few seconds for each loop, as shown in the sequence of operations.

094

ANAMORPHIC DISTORTIONS
To reveal the distorted images, hold the book with the bottom of the page towards you then lift the outside edge of the page about six inches from your nose, and look at the page at a very slanted angle. Close one eye – and everything will become clear.

097

RED AND GREEN CUBES
A solution with 22 touching cubes is shown. Five cubes can be placed on top of four sides of the red cube, as shown. Two more cubes can be placed to fill two holes on the opposite sides of the red cube. Other solutions have been found for 24 cubes as well. Can you think of them?

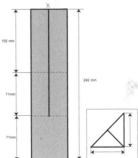

095

CUBE THROUGH CUBE
Prince Rupert's Cube

A maximum plane section cut in a unit cube is a rectangle with an area of V2, or 1.41+. The problem was first posed by C. Stanley Ogilvy and solved by Alan R.Hyde in 1956.

The simplest way to demonstrate that a square of a larger size than the side of a cube can fit the cube, is to imagine holding a side cube towards you so that one of its vertices is in the center. Its edges will outline a regular hexagon. Often it is wrongly assumed that cutting a cube to produce a regular hexagon is the maximum area, but its area is only 1.29+. Projecting one of the sides of the cube to the center of the hexagon we can see that its long diagonal is the same as that of the face of the cube, since this line has not been distorted. Revolving this projection into the plane of the hexagonal cross-section we can see that its middle corners will not reach the vertices of the hexagon. Tilting the square a bit, we can see all four of its corner to be inside the hexagon not touching its sides, allowing even a bigger square to fit. The largest square which fits inside a cube of unit side has each corner 1/4 distance from a corner of the cube.If a cube has sides of one unit a square hole can be drilled through with sides of almost 1.035 time the side of the cube. In order for the rest of the cube to stay in one pieces, the hole should be smaller.

For example, if you have a cube with sides of 100 mm, the size of the biggest square through it is 103.5 mm. A bigger cube of a slightly smaller than 103.5 mm side will pass through the unit side cube.

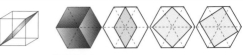

CUBE MAXIMUM AREA CUT

096

THIRTY COLOR CUBES

All the cubes have violet as the bottom face. The top faces get one of the remaining five colors in succession. Since the four blank faces are functionally equivalent, a third color can be placed on the front face freely. What remains are six permutations of the final three colors (since 3x2x1=6).

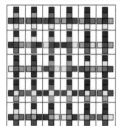

LINEAR CUBES

One possible solution is as shown.

BIG BROTHER

The credit for providing a complete solution to finding the eight cubes for any single cube selection goes to English mathematician John Horton Conway, who arranged the 30 cubes in a six-by-six table, giving all solutions of MacMahon's problem.

For example, if you want to select cube Bc and find the eight cubes for creating its bigger two-by-two-by-two replica, you go to its mirror cube Cb, and choose the remaining 8 cubes in Cb's line and column.

Puzzle 1	
1	= 1
2	= 2
3	= 2 + 1
4	= 4
5	= 4 + 1
6	= 4 + 2
7	= 4 + 2 + 1
8	= 8
9	= 8 + 1
10	= 8 + 2 + 1
11	= 8 + 2
12	= 8 + 4
13	= 8 + 4 +1
14	= 8 + 4 + 2
15	= 8 + 4 + 2 + 1
16	= 16
17	= 16 + 1
18	= 16 + 2
19	= 16 + 2 + 1
20	= 16 + 4
21	= 16 + 4 + 1
22	= 16 + 4 + 2
23	= 16 + 4 + 2 + 1
24	= 16 + 8
25	= 16 + 8 + 1
26	= 16 + 8 + 2
27	= 16 + 8 + 2 + 1
28	= 16 + 8 + 4
29	= 16 + 8 + 4 + 1
30	= 16 + 8 + 4 + 2
31	= 16 + 8 + 4 + 2 + 1
32	= 32
33	= 32 + 1
34	= 32 + 2
35	= 32 + 2 + 1
36	= 32 + 4
37	= 32 + 4 + 1
38	= 32 + 4 + 2
39	= 32 + 4 + 2 + 1
40	= 32 + 8

Puzzle 2		
1		= 1
2 + 1		= 3
3		= 3
4		= 3 + 1
5 + 3 + 1		= 9
6 + 3		= 9
7 + 3		= 9+1
8 + 1		= 9
9		= 9
10		= 9 + 1
11 + 1		= 9 + 3
12		= 9 + 3
13		= 9 + 3 + 1
14 + 9 + 3 + 1		= 27
15 + 9 + 3		= 27
16 + 9 + 3		= 27 + 1
17 + 9 + 1		= 27
18 + 9		= 27
19 + 9		= 27 + 1
20 + 9 + 1		= 27 + 3
21 + 9		= 27 + 3
22 + 9		= 27 + 3 + 1
23 + 3 + 1		= 27
24 + 3		= 27
25 + 3		= 27 + 1
26 + 1		= 27
27		= 27
28		= 27 + 1
29 + 1		= 27 + 3
30		= 27 + 3
31		= 27 + 3 + 1
32 + 3 + 1		= 27 + 9
33 + 3		= 27 + 9
34 + 3		= 27 + 9 + 1
35 + 1		= 27 + 9
36		= 27 + 9
37		= 27 + 9 + 1
38 + 1		= 27 + 9 + 3
39		= 27 + 9 + 3
40	=	27 + 9 + 3 + 1

BACHET'S WEIGHTS PROBLEM

The table shows the combinations of weights that achieve the solution.

(1) With weights allowed on one side of the scale only, and for weighing consecutive objects from 1 to 40 kilograms, you will need a binary set of six weights of 1kg, 2kg, 4kg, 8kg, 16kg, and 32kg. These weights are the first six powers of three: $2^0, 2^1, 2^2, 2^3, 2^4, 2^5$.

(2) With weights allowed on both sides of the scale, and for weighing consecutive objects from 1 to 40 kilograms, you will need a ternary set of weights (i.e. the first four powers of three: $3^0, 3^1, 3^2, 3^3$), that is: 1kg, 3kg, 9kg, and 27kg.

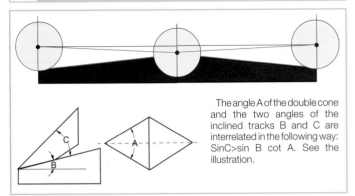

099

The angle A of the double cone and the two angles of the inclined tracks B and C are interrelated in the following way: SinC>sin B cot A. See the illustration.

ANTI-GRAVITY CONES

The double cone seemingly starts to go uphill, but is actually descending on the inclined track, as can be seen when the device is viewed from the side. As the double cone seemingly moves "up," the increasing width of the tracks lowers the cones so that in fact its center of gravity moves down. On the inclined double tracks the motion of the double cone is that of a mechanical oscillator or even a theoretical perpetual motion machine, with its center of gravity going up and down, to and fro; this oscillation may go on for a long time if the cones are heavy.

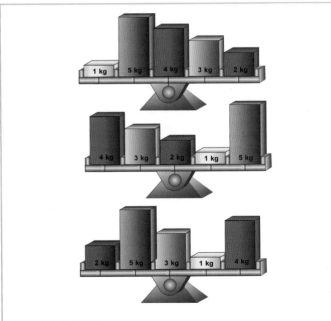

CHANCE BALANCE

There are six different equilibrium situations (three pairs of reflections). The probability of random equilibrium is 6/120= 1/20 or 5 per cent.

WEIGHT RANKING OF THREE OBJECTS

For three objects three weighings may be needed, as shown.

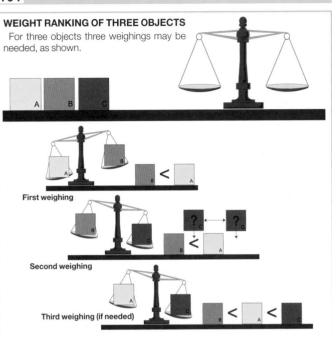

First weighing

Second weighing

Third weighing (if needed)

WEIGHT RANKING OF FOUR OBJECTS

For four objects five weighings may be needed, as shown.

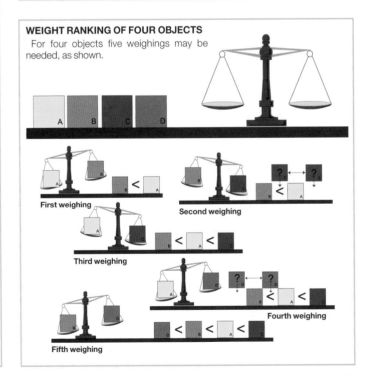

First weighing

Second weighing

Third weighing

Fourth weighing

Fifth weighing

WEIGHT RANKING OF FIVE OBJECTS

Five objects can be ranked with no more than seven weighings on a balance scale.

The general problem of ranking n weights with a minimum number of weighings was first proposed by Polish mathematician Hugo Steinhaus (1887–1972) in 1950. For 1 through 10, the minimal number of weighings are: 0, 1, 3, 5, 7, 10, 13, 16, 19, and 22.

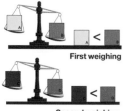

First weighing

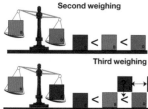

Second weighing

Third weighing

Fourth weighing   **Fourth weighing**

Fifth weighing   **Fifth weighing**

?

Sixth weighing   **Sixth weighing**

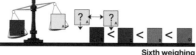 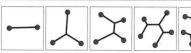

Seventh weighing

FOUCAULT PENDULUM

The apparent rotation of a pendulum varies with the latitude at which is installed. Its rate at points between the poles and the equator is equal to 15 degrees per hour multiplied by the sine of the latitude. This can be explained only by the fact that the Earth turns beneath the pendulum.

In the year 1543, Nicolaus Copernicus sent a copy of his book "On the revolutions of the Celestial Orbs" to Pope Paul III, with a note containing the historic understatement:

"I can easily conceive, that as soon as people learn that in this book I ascribe certain motions to the Earth, they will cry out at once that I and my theory should be rejected."

Some were still crying out in 1850, when Foucault was invited to arrange a scientific exhibit as part of the Paris Exhibition in 1851. From a dome of the Pantheon, Foucault hung a pendulum consisting of 200 feet of piano wire and a 30 kilogram cannon ball. On the floor, below the ball, he sprinkled a layer of fine sand. A stylus fixed to the bottom of the ball made a trace in the sand, thus recording the movement of the pendulum. At the end of an hour, the line in the sand turned 11 degrees and 18 minutes. This could be explained only on the basis that the earth had turned beneath the pendulum. Thus, the experiment finally settled the classic controversy once for all. Copernicus was vindicated!

102

THE ONE-TON PENDULUM

The boy can set the giant pendulum swinging by making repeated small pulls on the string. The pulls will make the pendulum swing in increasingly wide arcs if the rhythm of repetition of the small pulls is resonant. He should let it swing, then throw the magnet-string so the magnet attaches to the pendulum, and pull the magnet again at the moment when the pendulum ends its swings toward him. If he pulls too strongly, however, the thread will break.

104

MOONWALK PHOTO

There are no clouds on the moon, so the photo must be a fake. Clouds are water vapour floating in the air. The Moon has neither air nor water.

105

MOON, MERCURY AND STARS

There are one or possibly two stars inside the crescent covering the surface of moon: that would mean either that we are looking through the Moon or that there are stars between Moon and Earth. Both of these are impossible.

106

MINIMAL ROUTES PROBLEM

The minimal paths are trees – graphs with no closed loops in wich lines are joined together at angles of 120 degrees to one another.

107

ARCHIMEDES' PRINCIPLE

If the displaced waters were the same in both cases, the crown would be proven solid gold. But this was not the case. The crown displaced more water, proving that it was alloyed with a less dense metal than gold, the volume of which was greater than the volume of solid gold.

The crown turned out to be a fake, and Archimedes' fame grew as he made many other discoveries. The discovery of the fact that a body in liquid gains a lift (that is, it becomes lighter) due to the upward force called buoyancy, which is equal to the weight of the displaced liquid, established the science of hydrostatics.

108

PERCEPTION, ART AND ILLUSION

When you measure exactly, there are actually four different sized sculptures. But what we think we see is four that we assume to be the same size at different distances from us, plus one giant at the far end of the row. Our eyes compensate because they understand the effect of perspective, and they make us think there are only two sizes. In fact, the nearest and the farthest are actually the same size, which measurement confirms. Perspective can confuse our perception of the size and distance between objects. If two objects that are actually the same size are perceived as being at difference distances, the more distant one will look larger, as is strikingly demonstrated in this sculpture garden.

109

CONTRAST ILLUSION – HOW MANY COLOR SHADES ARE THERE?

The dividing lines between the color gradients allow you to detect the difference in shades. However, when the dividing lines are covered by pencils your perception is confused. It cannot detect a distinct edge and mistakenly assumes that each block is filled with a uniform shade of red.

AFTERIMAGE SPOTS

You can't really count the black spots at the intersections, because when you look directly at just one intersection where a black spot appears, the spot vanishes. In fact, none of the spots are really there.

The black spots appear as a result of a neural process called lateral inhibition, a phenomenon that amplifies the difference between light and dark. Light falling on the retina (the sensory membrane at the back of the eyes) excites the retina's neurons, which transmit impulses to the brain. In doing so, these neurons also kill the responses of neighboring visual cells (hence the term lateral inhibition) as a way of exaggerating subtle shades of light and helping the brain see details. So unless you're staring directly at a single intersection, the regular squares and lines kick these antagonistic functions into overdrive, fooling your brain into seeing black-gray spots where there aren't any. By looking directly at one intersection, however, you allow the process of lateral inhibition to work properly: The edges are clear.

The figure is known as a Hermann Grid, named after its designer L Hermann, who visualized it while reading a book about sound in 1870.

ILLUSORY SQUARES

The brain is filling in missing details. Our visual system has learned to analyze the defining contours of an object and then fill in the blanks to form the perception of the whole. This is an excellent shortcut, but under certain conditions it leads you to see what you expect to see, not what is really there.

The white subjective contours appear whiter than white but when the contours are examined closely they disappear. What is even more astonishing is the fact that we can distort subjective contours like real lines with optical illusions and play the same tricks with them as if they were real lines. We can distort them make them curved, and so on.

White square

Optical illusions can create confusions in our perceptions. In this case, we are seeing squares when there are none there.

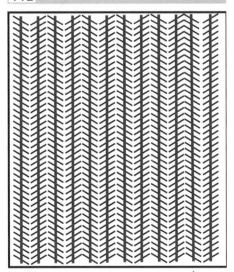

PARALLELS

In our slightly changed version the distortion of the last three parallel lines is compensated by correcting the illusion in changing the second line from right, as shown. Consequently we "see" as parallel only the three lines at right when in fact, they are the only lines that are not parallel, while all the rest of the lines are parallel.

NECKER CUBE LADYBIRD

(1) You can see the ladybird outside on the vertical wall of the cube.

(2) You can see it outside at the bottom of the cube.

(3) You can see it inside on the floor of the cube.

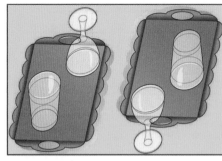

WINEGLASS ON A TRAY

The right-hand illustration is the inversion of the left-hand one. The wineglass appears to be on the tray in the left-hand illustration, but turn the book upside down and you will see that the glass is actually on the table, exactly as shown in the right-hand illustration.

CONVEX – CONCAVE

The obvious way is to rotate the image 180º. But also, as in a photographic negative, a similar effect can be achieved by turning the dark into light and the light into dark. In either case, the shadows will then become the highlights and it will appear that the direction of the source of light has changed.

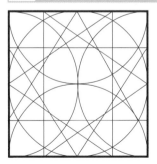

PATTERNS IN MATHEMATICS

Pairing patterns problem

All the colored tiles in our game are based on the same line pattern.

1	2	3	4	5
6	7	8	9	10
11	12	13	14	15
16	17	18	19	20
21	22	23	24	25
26	27	28	29	30

1	2	27	9	5
6	24	23	29	10
12	30	13	19	15
16	8	14	3	20
21	22	4	7	25
26	18	17	28	11

Left-hand page   Right-hand page

PAIRING PATTERNS PROBLEM

The solution to the pairing patterns problem is as shown.

LOVE CUBES

In the history of recreational mathematics there were 4 major puzzle crazes. The "Fifteen Puzzle", the "Tangram", the "Instant Insanity Puzzle", and the "Rubik's Cube".

The Love Cubes is one of the many new design variations of a century old puzzle, which is still marketed under different names. The object is to arrange the four cubes in a row so that all four colors (in any order) appear on each sides of the row, additionally also spelling out on all four sides the word 'LOVE'.

This won't be so easy as it may seem at first glance. There are over 40.000 different possible arrangements, and only one of these offers the solution to the puzzle.

The original version of the puzzle was designed and patented by Frederick A. Schossow of Detroit in 1900. His version was decorated with playing card images.

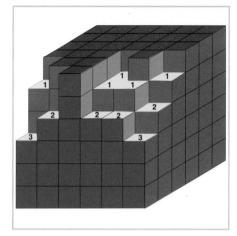

MISSING CUBES

Nineteen cubes are missing, as shown. Problems like these depend a great deal on our perception of depth, the three-dimensional effect afforded by perspective on a two-dimensional plane.

MISSING CUBE

Piece number 2 will complete the cube.

HARMONOGRAMS of Moscovich